ON THE MYSTERIOUS LEAP FROM THE MIND TO THE BODY

A Workshop Study on the Theory of Conversion

Edited by FELIX DEUTSCH, M.D.

)SOMATIC
PT IN
NALYSIS

IX DEUTSCH

)0

For several years Dr. Deutsch has
ed a workshop on psychosomatic
problems, with the collaboration of
he Boston Psychoanalytic Society.
This book is an outcome of his
workshop in which the participants
grappled with the most fundamental problem in psychosomatic research—the mind-body interrelationship. It is a specific contribution to the theory of conversion
both as a process and symptom.

The title of the book—actually a
quotation from Freud—indicates
the riddle surrounding the transformation of psychic impulses into
physical phenomena as well as the
dependence of mental phenomena
on physiological processes. The
papers and discussions included in
this volume scrutinize the formative stages of conversion; its relation to sensory experiences, symbol
formation, identification, and the
aggressive drives; its manifestations
in psychosis, homosexuality, and
disturbances of the menstrual cycle;
its role in determining choice of
symptoms. These theoretical and
clinical contributions, by focusing
on an all-inclusive concept of conversion, clarify many intricate problems and open up new avenues in
which further research is needed.

includes five lec-
Grinker, Kubie,
lfman and nine
originally pre-
on Psychoanalytic
tute. The main
e most advanced
hosomatic illness
tremendous theo-
particularly in the
ll the papers are
at the way toward
search and treat-
large all our con-
lity."—*Bulletin of
Clinic*

ly interested in
actions and famil-
analytic concepts
book informative
cts, hypotheses and
stions of our pres-
ge. Psychoanalysts
rested in learning
atic research has
psychoanalytic the-
of *the American
tion*

ll remain an im-
rk in the history of
elopment."—*Psycho-*

ON THE MYSTERIOUS LEAP
FROM THE MIND
TO THE BODY

With Contributions by

STANLEY COBB, M.D.   JAMES MANN, M.D.

FELIX DEUTSCH, M.D.   DORIS MENZER-BENARON, M.D.

HENRY M. FOX, M.D.   WILLIAM F. MURPHY, M.D.

PHILLIP H. GATES, M.D.   CECIL MUSHATT, M.D.

SANFORD GIFFORD, M.D.   ELVIN V. SEMRAD, M.D.

PETER H. KNAPP, M.D.   SAMUEL SILVERMAN, M.D.

ALFRED O. LUDWIG, M.D.   JEROME L. WEINBERGER, M.D.

AVERY WEISMAN, M.D.

ON THE MYSTERIOUS LEAP FROM THE MIND TO THE BODY

A Workshop Study on the Theory of Conversion

EDITED BY

FELIX DEUTSCH, M.D.

INTERNATIONAL UNIVERSITIES PRESS, INC.

NEW YORK

Copyright 1959, by International Universities Press, Inc.

Library of Congress Catalog Card Number: 59-8411

Manufactured in the United States of America

CONTENTS

v

PREFACE

This monograph originated from a workshop on psycho-somatic problems, with the collaboration of members of the Boston Psychoanalytic Society. One of these problems which seemed to be of particular interest was that of "the mysterious leap from the mind to the body," a phrase which Freud has coined when he referred to the riddle of the conversion process.[1]

There can be no doubt that Freud did not think of a dichotomy or a dualism. At the time when he conceived the theory of conversion, he considered only the transition from a psychic process into a bodily symptom as being enigmatic. However, he was always convinced that "mental mechanisms originate from physiological ones," and that both interact continually. He maintained that the instincts are the source of the energies which give the mind-body interrelationship the specific expression characteristic for each individual. "All psychic phenomena, instinctual needs with their drives for gratification and the reactions to frustration are not mere thoughts but are due to physiologic processes."

Freud never gave up the hope that some time in the future there will be found a comprehensive fusion of both the physiological and psychological phenomena. Conceptual and methodological concepts in psychoanalysis must be scrutinized

[1] See, for instance, *A General Introduction to Psychoanalysis*, p. 229.

vii

continually. These were the reasons why I proposed the topic of the conversion process for further clarification.

On the occasion of Freud's 100th birthday I had dedicated to his memory an essay on "The Riddle of the Mind-Body Correlations" which was accepted by the participants of the workshop as a starting point for the discussion. Thereby the ground was laid for a free exchange of opinions, which in the course of the past three years became crystallized in a series of papers read at a scientific meeting of the Boston Psychoanalytic Society and at a Panel on the Theory of the Conversion Process at the meeting of the American Psychoanalytic Association in San Francisco in May, 1958.

FELIX DEUTSCH, M.D.

ACKNOWLEDGMENT

In the preparation of this book I have depended on the unfailing cooperation of the participants of the workshop on the "Theory of Conversion." They were at liberty to express their critical viewpoints. Their contributions, in which they join me in the validation of my concept of the conversion process, belong to the main content of this book.

Acknowledgment is made with thanks to the Editor of the *Psychoanalytic Quarterly* for the permission to reprint my article "A Footnote to Freud's 'Fragment of an Analysis of a Case of Hysteria'" as well as to the Editors of the *Acta Orientalia* for their permission to reprint my article "The Riddle of the Mind-Body Correlations."

I wish to express my appreciation to my publisher Dr. A. S. Kagan for his continual interest in my writings, and particularly to Mrs. Lottie Maury Newman for her assistance in editing the manuscript.

I also feel indebted to my secretary Miss Fritzi Zohn for her endeavors to keep the manuscript as free as possible from any stylistic and typographical errors.

FELIX DEUTSCH, M.D.

Part I

Part 1

1.

THE RIDDLE OF THE MIND-BODY CORRELATIONS[1]

In Memory of Freud's Hundredth Birthday

FELIX DEUTSCH, M.D.

The centenary of Freud's birth certainly seems an appropriate occasion to reflect on how it came about that Medicine, the mother science, almost lost her most brilliant child, Psychoanalysis; or should we say, why the mother science rejected this child and why for such a long time the child did not want to return home, and disclaimed its origin. Now, many foster parents offered him adoption. However, it seems as if both mother and child begin to recognize that they are blood-related. Hence it is time to take stock and to examine briefly what they have in common and whether they are in need of each other. In doing so one must search for motives leading to their alienation. That cannot be done without an inquiry into Freud's attitude toward medicine.

Looking back upon the attacks against analysis made by some so-called unprejudiced scientists, or upon one's own unswerving defense of Freud's analytic theses, and remembering the years of almost being ostracized for it, one cannot help feeling reconciled and pleased that the time of isolation

1 Reprinted from *Acta Medica Orientalia (Israel Med. Journal)*, Vol. XV, No. 6-7, June-July 1956.

and of the "ivory tower" is apparently over. However, one is still warned against overoptimism in view of the many who have climbed the analytic "band wagon" either to make public spectacle of analysis or to refute the "orthodoxy."

Freud was ready to revise and restate the formulations of his own ideas. He despised all deification and conformity to autocratic orders; he distrusted the "Yes-men." His aim was to convince through facts based on clinical observation. It is well known how he suffered when some of his closest collaborators went astray. He was not angry with them; all he did was to leave them behind and to continue on his own way unerringly. He did not permit any misuse or wrong interpretation of the principles of analysis. He drew a sharp line between the convinced followers of psychoanalysis and the impetuous reformists who impatiently wanted to run ahead of him with independent theories. Freud was accustomed to letting his ideas mature in his mind for a long time before presenting them as the product of long deliberation. He became used to waiting, but knew his time would come.

Some of us who as exponents in medicine had taken over the role of a liaison officer with psychoanalysis had for this reason often difficulties in maintaining the recognized status in our own field, and in spinning the threads of the analytic concepts onto the other side, since every dealing with the analytic group was sufficient cause for discrimination. This mutual hostility had reasons which cannot be separated from Freud's own attitude toward official medicine.

It is astounding to read in Freud's autobiography (1925) that he should have turned to medicine: "Neither at that time, nor indeed later in my life," he writes, "did I feel any particular predilection for the career of a physician. . . . The various branches of medicine proper, apart from psychiatry, had no attraction for me." However, he admits that he had a "medical conscience which felt pleased at having arrived at the conclusion" that by deriving hysteria from sexuality he had been "going back to the very beginning of medicine." Thus the investigation of neurasthenia which led to the claim that this mental disorder is due to the direct expression of disturbance of the sexual function "cost me, it is true, my popularity as a doctor."

Here begins the rift, because "I hoped that I had filled a gap in medical science which in dealing with a function of such great biological importance had failed to take into account injuries beyond those caused by infection or by gross anatomical lesions."

In this attempt to close the gap between physiologic and mental processes he had previously failed, since he found it impossible to explain the psychic apparatus in terms of brain physiology. "Research has afforded irrefutable proof that mental activity is bound up with the function of the brain as with that of no other organ. . . . But every attempt to deduce from these facts a localization of mental processes, every endeavor to think of ideas as stored up in nerve cells and of excitations as passing along nerve-fibers, has completely miscarried."

From here on, Freud went his own way. Medicine as such remained his profession, but no longer as the field of research on how to fill the gap from the physiologic side. He denied himself the interest in what was happening on this side of the border. He left it, knowing that others would take up the thread. Many tried, and much research has been carried on in this direction, but to this very day we are still far from closing the "mysterious leap" (Freud, 1916-1917, p. 229) from the psychic to the physiologic.

Following the blunt rejection of his concept of the sexual basis of hysteria by the leading psychiatrists and neurologists, Freud renounced any further public controversies but turned his back on them, so to speak, without reconciliation or concession. This embittered his adversaries all the more. It almost seemed as if Freud had been glad to have gotten rid of them, since they were only a hindrance in what he had to accomplish.

Freud never again attended any of the meetings of medical societies after having been denounced in public.

Although this separation of Freud from his medical past would be sufficiently explained by the events, and his later attitude toward lay analysis could be regarded as the natural consequence of these developments, the posthumous discovery of the manuscript "Project for a Scientific Psychology" (1895) shed even more light on the motives behind his irreconcilable standpoint toward medicine.

In this paper Freud appears to have made a last attempt to explain mental activities in terms of brain physiology. In spite of its scope it was written almost in one stroke—in a kind of irresistible passion, a condition which later on Freud himself could not quite explain. It was something like a farewell to his credo of the past. At any rate, that manuscript would have remained lost forever, except for the indefatigable efforts of Madame Marie Bonaparte. Freud never made any mention of this work in his writings. The disappointment at having failed in his attempt to incorporate the mental processes into the biological matrix genetically could be endured only by a man of Freud's stamina.

In a kind of apology he wrote Fliess in the late 1890's: "I have no desire at all to leave psychology hanging in the air with no organic basis. But, beyond a feeling of conviction [that there must be such a basis] I have nothing, either theoretical or therapeutic, to work on, and so I must behave as if I were confronted by psychological factors only. I have no idea yet why I cannot fit it together [the psychologic and the organic]" (Freud, 1887-1902). However, he always emphasized—as Kris writes in the introduction to the Fliess letters—"that the terminology of psychoanalysis was provisional, valid only until it could be replaced by a physiologic terminology. The psychic entities of psychoanalysis are described as organisms and characterized by their functions, just as physiologic organs are."

Freud never left any doubt that "mental phenomena are to a large extent dependent upon physiologic ones, and both have the most powerful effects on each other." He maintained that the instincts are the source of the energies on which the mind-body processes depend, and that the human organism is a mind-body entity. "Emotions and instinctual gratifications and feelings of frustration do not consist of mere thoughts but of physical alterations."

But a research man arriving at a point where his research tools lead him no further does not give up or start to pray; rather by renouncing to make a frontal attack at one point he continues the research at another one. That is what Freud did. With his creative passion he began to build the edifice of psychoanalysis.

Freud was always apprehensive that psychoanalysis as a method of psychologic investigation of the mind and body might become the exclusive tool of medicine. In his opinion this would have meant a regrettable impoverishment of analysis. He expressed this attitude clearly in the statement: "The medical degree does not give to doctors a historical claim to the monopoly of analysis," and he continued: "In fact, a physician who has not been through a *special training* is—in spite of his diploma—a layman in analysis, and a *non-physician* who has been suitably *trained* can, with occasional reference to a physician, carry out the analytic treatment not only of children, but also of neurotics."

Freud did not specify what kind of suitable training of the "layman" he had in mind when he expressed in these terms his antagonism against the medical profession. But he certainly went further when he stepped beyond the borders of psychology to metapsychology, "a method of approach in which every mental process is considered in relation to three coordinates which I described as dynamic, topographical, and economic, respectively."

One must admit that without this concept and without that of the unconscious, we would never have been able to find our way into the darkness where the mental processes begin to condition and to co-regulate the biological ones. These concepts have guided us behind the "iron curtain" of the human mind. For anyone standing in front of this closed door, the mind-body problem would have remained an insoluble one if the magic key of the unconscious had not been discovered.

The uninitiated had to turn on their heels in discouragement or they simply denied that there was a problem at all, as a renowned scientist, the physicist Planck (1949) did in his *Scientific Autobiography:* "It is an experience annoying as can be, to find after a long time spent in toil and effort, that the problem which has been preying on one's mind is totally incapable of any solution at all—either because there exists no indisputable method to unravel it—or because considered in the cold light of reason, it turns out to be absolutely void of all meaning—in other words, it is a phantom-problem."

Although he admitted that there are not only conscious states of the mind and that "many processes, even the most decisive ones, must be taking place in the subconscious mind," Planck declared that they are beyond the reach of scientific analysis. "For there exists no science of the unconscious mind. It would be a contradiction in terms, a self-contradiction. One does not know that which is subconscious. Therefore, all problems concerning the sub-conscious are phantom-problems." Based on this conviction he felt justified to call the psychological and the physiological viewpoints incompatible. "We cannot judge our mental processes"—he went on to say—"directly from the physiological viewpoint any more than we can examine a physical process from the psychological viewpoint. For, the examination of the psychosomatic processes will yield entirely different results, accord-ing to whether the psychologic viewpoint is taken as the basis of observation . . . . It is therefore impossible to gain first-hand information about physical and mental processes from any single viewpoint . . . . There exist only physical processes *or* mental processes, but never processes which are physical *and* mental . . . . They are the selfsame processes, only viewed from two diametrically opposite directions. This statement is the answer to the riddle, how one is to conceive the fact that two types of processes so different from each other as the physical and the mental are so closely inter-linked. The body-mind problem has been recognized as another phantom-problem."

Only the denial of the science of the Unconscious, the dis-regard of this fundament of psychoanalysis, can lead to the erroneous statement that the mind-body problem is non-existent. Of course, there is no psychophysiological parallel-ism, but there is a continuous mental process acting on the physiological ones which can be defined. We cannot measure the mental stimulus—but we can judge the psychic processes indirectly from its effect on the physiologic one, i.e., on the body.

Freud never ceased to search for the "mysterious leap" from a mental process to a somatic innervation—although he rather pessimistically thought it might never be fully com-prehended. In spite of that, however, he never gave up the hope that some time in the future there must be a compre-hensive fusion of both the biological and psychological con-cepts. He always adhered to a "universal monism." During the last scientific meetings in his house he repeatedly stated that he had to hurry up, because "endocrinology" was already at the heels of analysis. However, he was able to complete his task.

Since Freud's death the pathways have been greatly wid-ened. The science called "psychosomatic medicine" has not only become a domain of psychoanalysis, but almost deserves the name of "psychoanalytic medicine." It is the beginning of a reconciliation between analysis and medicine. The "mysterious leap" from the mind into the body—that riddle which Freud began to solve—seems to be nearer to its solution on his hundredth birthday.

2.

IS THE TERM
"MYSTERIOUS LEAP" WARRANTED?

INTRODUCTION

When the preceding paper was read to the membership of
the workshop, it became apparent that there was a divergence
of opinions as to whether Freud's term "the mysterious leap"
was still valid, and whether the known psychophysiological
facts have clarified the "mystery" which once puzzled Freud.
For these reasons each of the participants was asked to express
his preliminary opinion.

STANLEY COBB:

I believe that Freud's statement about the "mysterious
leap" from the mind into the body is today meaningless.
There is no separation between psyche and soma; therefore
there can be no leap. Felix Deutsch has brought this problem
up for specific discussion by asking, in the case of hysteria,
how one can explain "the leap from a mental process to a
somatic innervation." I maintain that there is no leap at all
for one who believes that mind is not a supernatural phenomenon but is *the active integration of the billions of nerve
cells and hundreds of cell masses of the living brain.* Mind
is the integration in action, the relationship of one part of the
brain to another. The physical integers or units are the nerve
impulse. Mind is a function of the brain just as contraction
is a function of muscle or as circulation is a function of the
blood-vascular system.

When one thinks of "circulation" one thinks of heart, arteries, veins, capillaries and the blood with its oxygen, hormones, enzymes and food. Circulation is the movement of all this, a living process with a time factor. Mind is no more supernatural than circulation, it is merely a more complex conception and harder to grasp because of the commonly accepted dualistic philosophy that permeates our present civilization. Few physicians think this through. Even among psychiatrists many only pay lip-service to the monistic concept, few have disciplined themselves to the point where they have actually stopped thinking dualistically. It is no easy task to discard habits of thought that are centuries old and embedded in the idioms of our language (Cobb, 1957).

Modern biologists who have concerned themselves with the problem of mind (Herrick, 1956; Sinnott, 1957; Huxley, 1953), and neurologists (Brain, 1950), psychiatrists (Slater, 1953), and psychologists (Hebb, 1957), who have taken philosophy seriously and thought the problem through, have become convinced monists. No metaphysical concepts are needed. As Julian Huxley (1953) expresses it, "mind is not a pale epiphenomenon . . . but an operative part of life's mechanism . . . . Mental activity is tied in with cerebral activity. It only goes on in conjunction with brains, and only with brains that are working properly." Sinnott (1957) puts it even more dynamically, saying, "Mind is more than mere behavior; whether due to internal genetic factors or to outer environmental pressures, the same sort of self-regulation to ends is displayed that we see in embryology and physiology. Mind is what guides behavior to ends set up in living systems." Sir Henry Cohen (1952) has gone so far as to say: "The ultimate goal of Science is a universal monism." When trying to use one's intellect in such company, concepts such as "organic versus functional" become trivial colloquialisms and terms like "functional psychoses" and "organic personality" become barbarous clinical slang.

To change from the more general to the more specific point of view, one can consider the anatomical mechanism that makes possible the "leap from a mental process to a somatic innervation." As an example of a "mental process" one can take a memory. It is known that memories are stored in the brain, but by what means is still a matter of speculation. Nevertheless, a stored memory can be normally aroused by an appropriate stimulus. It even may be aroused by an abnormal stimulus in special cases, for example, a stimulating electrode in the hands of a surgeon. Penfield's experiments (1958) on the human cortex of the temporal lobe have proved this.

Normally, however, the appropriate stimulus is a series of nerve impulses that arouse the memory and cause it to modify the nerve impulses which later impinge on an effector brain mechanism to cause behavior: the motor cortex in the case of motor behavior, the hypothalamus if the behavior is expressed through the autonomic system. A simple example of the latter would be Pavlov's salivary conditioned reflex; for motor reactions in striated muscle, a conditioned flexion of the leg as described by Liddell (1956) would suffice. From the conditioned reflex one can progress to more and more complex memories. These condition all our adult behavior, normal or abnormal, which are modified by a whole lifetime of experiences. In other words, there is no mystery about the anatomical and physiological mechanisms available for transforming perceptions into action. The practical difficulties of understanding lie in the unique experiences of each individual, and in the psychological understanding of their enormous complexity. The mystery is how memories are stored.

HENRY M. FOX:

In an article entitled "Does Consciousness Exist?" published in 1904, William James states that "the dualism connoted by such double-barrelled terms as 'experience,' 'phe-nomenon,' 'datum,' 'Vorfindung'—terms which in philosophy at any rate tend more and more to replace the single-barrelled terms of 'thought' and 'thing' . . . is still preserved . . . but re-interpreted, so that instead of being mysterious and elusive it becomes verifiable and concrete. It is an affair of relations, it falls outside, not inside, the single experience considered, and can always be particularized and defined." James adds that "the entering wedge for this more concrete way of understanding the dualism was fashioned by Locke when he made the word 'idea' stand indifferently for thing and thought and by Berkeley when he said that what common sense means by realities is exactly what the philosopher means by ideas."

The dichotomy of body and mind represents a special case of the more general dichotomy of thing and thought. These dichotomies are misleading because they verbally allude to a split which does not correspond to the unitary nature of experience and of the living organism. Therefore, the so-called "mysterious leap" from the mind to the soma represents an invitation to reunite certain ways of describing the organism which itself was never actually divided. That mental function has unconscious as well as conscious modalities in no way alters the fact that one organism (whether thought of as physical or mental, responding consciously, unconsciously, or both) undergoes only one experience at a time.

The same experience of the organism may, however, be observed in differing contexts, and certain aspects of organismal function may be selected for consideration within the appropriate frame of reference. Thus the behavior of constellations of electrons, homeostatic balances of electrolytes, changes in cellular growth and activity, alterations in the respiratory or digestive function, cortical stimulation or inhibition, perceptual changes and the emergence or repression of memories represent aspects of the same organism at different levels of integration. There is no mysterious leap;

and, in fact, it behooves us to look well before making an unwitting leap from one frame of reference to another which can only lead to confusion.

Since the organism functions as an integrated unit, however, measurable balances at different levels may correspond and can be compared. Breathing may, for instance, vary concurrently with remembering, but each requires a different type of observation as a basis for establishing a meaningful and reliable correlation. On the other hand, breathing does not become transmuted into remembering even though a gasp may accompany a recollection. Thus abundant opportunities invite imaginative attempts to establish meaningful correlations of data obtained by appropriate methods from different levels of integration without any need to resort to a mysterious leap.

PHILLIP H. GATES:

My view of the mysterious leap is that Freud's original usage in the "Rat Man" paper (1909) stresses the leap remaining incomprehensible: a statement that need not be construed so strictly now. There are many areas in biology, physiology, and psychoanalysis which may seem to have been exhaustively studied but which can be restudied with profit. The real hazard, as I see it, is the unconscious application of the old law of parsimony, the formulation that it is scientifically unsound to set up more than one hypothesis, a principle that is also known as Occam's razor, in studying the various "leaps" from mind to body, from body to mind, from mind to mind, and from body to body. In this sense, there are no mysteries, only things that are insufficiently understood.

SANFORD GIFFORD:

During these discussions I have recognized more clearly my preference for a monistic concept of mind and body, essentially in agreement with Dr. Cobb's remark that there is "no leap, no mystery." When I recall my first intense interest in psychosomatic problems, as a psychiatric resident, it seems to me now that I was probably attracted by an unrecognized fantasy of the omnipotence of the mind, by a tendency toward overvaluing psychic processes and denying the importance of organic ones. Although even then I thought I believed in a unitary concept of mind and body, my actual belief was an oversimplified assumption that unconscious conflicts "caused" physiological changes and eventually structural alterations in the body.

Since that time, influenced by Dr. Deutsch and others, as well as my own clinical experiences, I have come to accept all mental and physical phenomena as different aspects of a single process of biological adaptation, observed from different points of view and studied by different methods. Manifest behavior, conscious and unconscious affects, intellectual and symbolic processes, sensory perceptions and motor discharge, mechanisms of physiological regulation, integrative functions of the central nervous system and biochemical changes at a cellular level—all coexist at any given time in the life of the organism, although some phenomena may be observed directly, some measured quantitatively in the laboratory, and others inferred by psychoanalytic deduction. In certain situations, when one component is altered, the concept of cause and effect still applies, but the complex, synchronous interrelationships among all components that result from such a change cannot be reduced to a simple duality. These situations occur, for example, when illness, drugs or trauma disturb biochemical processes, when the body ego preserves the phantom of an amputated limb, or when unsatisfied instinctual needs create hallucinatory objects of gratification. In many situations, however, the mental and physical components cannot be sharply differentiated, or the biochemical substrate of the psychic phenomenon cannot be detected by available methods, as in the interrelationships between a chronic instinctual conflict and a disturbance in homeostatic regulation, or between the visual image, the nerve impulse and its symbolic representation.

Much of the discussion emphasizing the existence of "the leap" and maintaining that the mind-body problem is not a "phantom problem" was concerned with a relatively late phase of infantile maturation, with the occurrence of symbolization, the differentiation of the self from external reality, and the development of object relations. Apparently this occurs at about the third month with the appearance of the smiling response, which represents, according to René Spitz (1946), the precursor of subsequent object relations and the first direct communication between the mother and the infant. In the previous undifferentiated phase of ego development, however, many adaptive biological patterns have been developing, from simple stimulus-response patterns of crying and receiving food to highly organized adaptations to a twenty-four-hour rhythm of rest and activity. During this period psychic processes and bodily activity are inseparable, but I believe that the newborn infant, the fetus, or even the unicellular organism may be said to possess an ego, if it is defined as the sum total of all adaptive biological processes that mediate between inner needs and the environment, that act to maintain the life and bodily integrity of the organism. With further maturation, ontogenetically or phylogenetically, this primitive ego becomes more highly differentiated, and the psychic aspects of these integrative functions are referred to by the abstraction "ego," and the physiological aspects by the abstraction "homeostasis." This seems to be a convenience, in terminology and usage, without implying a separation, a true duality or an exclusive cause-and-effect relationship. A discussion of the undifferentiated phase when "ego" and "homeostasis" and manifest behavior are inseparable, of the earliest differentiation of the self and its parts as external objects, subsequently reunited with the body ego by symbolization, explores an important theoretical area, but I still have difficulty in understanding how these complex and interesting interrelationships imply the existence of a "leap" between mind and body.

PETER H. KNAPP:

The words "mysterious leap from the mind to the soma" are a metaphor. In my opinion, the question should not be whether the leap "exists," or whether it exists more in our "present-day" world, but: how useful is this metaphor? To what extent does it help us to bring order into experience?

Immediately we are involved in the question of levels of discourse. The levels can be distinguished. At the *clinical-pragmatic* level "mind" and "body" are frequent terms. All patients have vague, empirical, naïve fantasy conceptions of something they call their body and something they call their mind. Phenomena that appear to originate in one area seem to lead to effects in the other. These fantasy conceptions are important in the thinking of individuals and are useful in understanding many of the clinical data which they present. A second level is the *scientific-philosophic*. Here the problem is entirely different. "Mind" and "body" are concepts. Conceivably they could represent different "essences," as they have been conceived in the dualistic tradition since Plato. However, the question is not settled. Certainly it is far from proven that such a dualistic view, whether conceived as a complete dualism or as psychophysical parallelism, is the most profitable or generally valid metaphysical framework. There is a strong modern philosophic trend, represented by James, Bergson, Whitehead, Dewey, Northrop, and others, to take an opposite point of view and to develop a monistic approach, which insists that mind and body are only aspects of an underlying unified reality.

In this workshop, it seems to me that basic differences arose from failure to recognize these levels of discourse. Dr. Deutsch and those associated in their thinking with him, in so far as I grasped them, represented the clinical-pragmatic point of view. Their language was that of clinical psychoanalysis; their attempt was to understand the origins of what we experience as mind and body, and in particular to trace the orgins of the process of symbolization.

Dr. Deutsch contributes to our understanding of psychic life, of the ontogenesis of certain mental functions, and in particular of the role of human relationships in determining psychosomatic phenomena; and his contribution is brilliant and stimulating. It should be elaborated and should lead to further clinical and experimental studies of development.

Others in the group seemed to be talking at a different level of discourse, namely, the scientific-philosophic, as I have sketched it. The chief spokesman was Dr. Cobb. His presentation did not deal with developmental phenomena. His language and frame of reference were that of general science. He argued that mind had no locus, was not an organ, but was a function of the total organism. He spoke of personal difficulty in achieving a monistic point of view. In so doing he implied, though he did not make explicit, a suggestion in which I am personally interested, namely that one reason for the difficulty most people have in attaining such a unitary view may spring from universal, ingrained affective attitudes —the emotional roots of dualism. My own feeling is that man's view of himself as composed of two separate parts, "mind" and "body," is essentially an ambivalent fantasy, one deserving of further study, perhaps by the same approach with which Dr. Deutsch has so well illuminated many other "mental" and "physical" phenomena.

ALFRED O. LUDWIG:

If one accepts the fact that there is no mind-body dichotomy, it becomes difficult to adhere to the idea of a "mysteri-

ous leap." The phenomena that we observe are manifestations
of the same process occurring simultaneously in both the
psychic and somatic spheres. They may be visible in only one,
although, for example, obsessions appear to be purely psychic
manifestations, there must be a biologic reaction underlying
the psychic phenomenon. Freud's concept of a "leap" implied
a dichotomy which is no longer tenable. Phenomena always
manifest themselves in both spheres and are observable when
we are in possession of the proper methods to do so.

WILLIAM F. MURPHY:

The leap from the mind into the body can no longer be
considered "mysterious." It is, in reality, a leap from one
level of abstraction to another, that of the mind being of a
much higher order of hazy complexity than that of the body.
In the past, mind has always meant conscious mentality. The
concept of unconscious mental processes has made the problem of the leap obsolete. One "leap" is that from conscious
to unconscious mental phenomena. An understanding of this
"leap" will be obtained mainly in psychoanalytically struc-
tured explorations of the phenomena of consciousness, memory, and experiencing; e.g., how are intersensory perceptions
related to consciousness and how do they act as focal points
which tie together, telescope or condense isolated experiences
into the patterned structures we call memories?

Felix Deutsch, in his studies of intersensory perception
patterns, has pointed the way to proceed in our studies. It is
my belief that the term "intersensory perception" highlights
the fact that one type of sensory perception from the point
of view of a mental apparatus has little if any meaning except
in terms of another. Thus a basic relationship in the study of
mental processes is that between a sensory organ and the apperceptive ego viewed as an integrate of all the sensory systems patterned and modified by constitutional, dispositional,
expositional and temporal factors. Such an integrate can be

considered an epiphenomenon. This does not explain consciousness. In all probability, there are as many types, degrees and stages of consciousness as there are simple and multiple intersensory perceptions. It may be that consciousness arises as the level of complexity of the intersensory perceptions due to developmental and experiential factors reaches a certain threshold. It is difficult to conceive consciousness in any other term except as an epiphenomenon in the way a molecule is an epiphenomenon of a combination of atoms. The concept of the unconscious has to a degree furnished us with the means of understanding the relativity of soma, mind, consciousness, and personality. An increase in the complexity of consciousness leads to new thresholds of development and new epiphenomena, such as the ability to deal with abstractions, etc.

An understanding of the role played by the intersensory perceptions that are involved in the repetitive re-enactment of traumatic events is of fundamental importance in developing a further understanding of the function and meaning of such concepts as the mind, sensory overstimulation, the memory trace, and eventually of such complexities as personality and certain nonverbal aspects of character structure. The way a person perceives the world is as much a part of his character as the way he behaves. A study of what is perceived, and how it is done, is important for the understanding of the complex elements involved in the development of mind-body relationships. Studies on the abolition of intersensory perception have already yielded much valuable data on the disintegration of the ego and varying stages of consciousness.

The drive toward unification, integration, increase in complexity, and the formation of larger and more unstable units manifests itself in the spheres of both body and mind. It culminates in the desire of everyone to unify and integrate the totality of his individual experiences. This drive has been called "Eros." Its manifestations can be followed from the simplest condensations of primal energy into hydrogen atoms up to the individual mind. Each level of complexity is accompanied by an increase in rarity, until a level is reached at which each mind is such a complex phenomenon that it can be considered a unique integrate of substance, sensation, and experience.

The term "mind" is a holistic concept embracing conscious and unconscious mental phenomena as well as identity and character. As body and mind abstractions are of a different order of complexity, the body-mind duality concept is, in all its naïveté, a useful and necessary aid to our understanding inasmuch as the apperceptive ego must disintegrate as well as integrate percepts to effect an understanding. Each ego can discover and understand its object world only by the fact that it has selected from a uniform mass of bodily sensory percepts certain ones peculiar to that object, and all objects differ from each other because there are contained in each of them different questions of knowledge that evoke different patterns of perception. The ego thus has different ways of referring minor and major bodily sensory perceptions concerning these objects to more holistic concepts, thereby ordering and mastering them. In this way, understanding and consciousness can be related to the ego's satisfaction of its needs through the modulation of intra- as well as intersensory perceptions.

The body image is an important concept in the body-mind relationship. For the sake of simplicity, it can be considered the physiological representative of the ego. Its manifestations, like those of the iceberg with most of its bulk below the surface of the water, are not readily apparent and tend to be neglected. The more obvious sociological, interpersonal and inanimate objects of the inner world have appeared more important in the past. The work of Felix Deutsch on intersensory perception, of Leo Berman on depersonalization, perception and object relations, of Kubie on the ego and

organization of the brain, and of Hendrick on ego development, is indicative of the beginning of a more comprehensive
understanding of the libido theory and ego development in
terms of body-image participation.

The relationship of the primitive "mind" or ego nucleus to
the body must be, at first, a global, unitary, diffuse one,
highly colored by the sensory perceptions entailed by the
birth process and a beginning series of new and more dis-
crete relationships with the outside world. The nipple-mouth
relationship stems from the older body-ego nucleus pattern
of relationship and foreshadows the stool-sphincter, phallus-
hand, and the child-mother relationships to come. The body
image is thus the physiological mirror image of the ego, just
as much as the ego is a projection of the body surface. Such
conceptions can be unified only up to a certain point of
usefulness.

As Felix Deutsch has so clearly demonstrated, the ego
constructs and integrates the body image according to its
over-all needs; i.e., the nature of the body image changes
from time to time and is largely dependent upon the defensive needs of the ego. Such changes can be observed in a
striking form in cases of phantom-limb pain. Each libidinal
phase and diagnostic grouping has its own body image. The
mouth body-image of the schizo-affective psychotic, the stool
body-image of the compulsive, and the phallic body-image of
the hysteric are as well known as the "Charles Atlas" ego-
ideal body-image of the adolescent.

Returning to the original theme of the "leap," we can
conclude that the mind-body problem is closely related to
the ego-body-image problem. From this point of view, the
body image is the basis of our understanding of the psychological universe and the means by which the ego communi-
cates with both the inner and outer worlds. In this light, the
"leap" is a developmental abstraction, useful as a poetic figure of speech, but a philosophical trap for the unwary.

CECIL MUSHATT:

I find the term "mysterious leap" quite understandable, and perhaps even necessary. Misunderstanding arises from seeing in it the implication of a dualism of mind and body which does not exist.

The term is useful inasmuch as it states the existence of two different modes of expression for the same internal event. The gap between psyche and soma becomes more apparent than real with the use of the concept of the conversion process as elaborated in this workshop. The concept helps immeasurably to show how mental and physical activity become synonymous in their representations.

Some difficulty arose for me in the beginning in approaching the problem in this way, because it necessitated the realization and the acceptance of the hypothesis that symbolization, primitive though it may be at the time, begins with the beginning of life.

ELVIN V. SEMRAD:

The person as a psychobiological unit is an entity available for study without the necessity of postulating a leap from body to mind or vice versa. We suffer some limitations in our present methods and our capacity to conduct such studies. In the same paper (1909) in which Freud mentions the "leap" and implies its mystery, he apologizes two paragraphs later for the limited amount of data he presented, saying he recognizes these limitations but will do what he can with it.

I think there is a great deal known about the body and mind correlations, but their studies have still been limited. Much has been added to our knowledge by the study of the unconscious—an investigation available only to those who took the trouble to learn something about it. The study of the unconscious—and more studies at the conscious level are also needed—of bodily sensations and bodily responses, particularly if integrated with other methods, will enable us to study man as an integrated unit. The results of such research will depend on the skills of the investigator and on the methods he uses. It would be desirable if all the necessary skills would be combined in one person.

By and large, we are here embarked on the study of sensory perceptions and their vicissitudes in development. Some of the problems in this area are crucial. One is the need to learn when symbolization takes place; and two, what aspects of relationships are thereby created which enable the individual to achieve a consolidated body ego? In essence, what bodily processes initiated by sensations from within or without should not remain unfinished and unintegrated?

One can add more questions: Is symbolization a source of body-ego strength and has it an integrative function? How much of it is reflected in the organ symptoms and how far are they influenced by it? Does it endow the individual with an apparatus for dealing better with life, and in his interpersonal relationships, or does it also provoke unpleasant sensations that disturb his psychic equilibrium? For me it is less a question of a leap than that of a gap, i.e., in our knowledge of the conversion process, which has to be filled. All depends on whether the right methods will be chosen for its investigation.

JEROME L. WEINBERGER:

I essentially agree with Dr. Deutsch that the basic conditioning or sensitization has occurred in the earliest infancy and becomes more and more established within the body ego or body image, so that it remains there in readiness, latently, to become manifest under conditions of appropriate and sufficient stress, to appear as bodily or organ symptoms. In a sense the leap never occurs. It has been there all along. It only appears as though it were a leap because the repressed psychic process and its structural antecedents in the body ego and in the instinctual conflicts are not apparent behind the organ symptoms, which reflect them as a mirror.

FELIX DEUTSCH:

From these statements it appears that a plan has to be worked out to find a common denominator which could serve as a basis for a reconciliation of these different viewpoints. Above all, it seems most advisable to *survey historically Freud's conceptualization of the conversion symptom.* That promises to be more the "right step," since the vast literature of the past twenty-five years dealing with this problem has shown that some authors were of the opinion that the term "conversion" should be abandoned, while others recommended only that its use should be limited to its original meaning, or should be broadened and applied to all kinds of neuroses.

3.

SURVEY OF FREUD'S WRITINGS ON THE CONVERSION SYMPTOM

FELIX DEUTSCH, M.D. and
ELVIN V. SEMRAD, M.D.

The following selections of Freud's views pertinent to the conversion process were chosen to serve as a background for the chapters of this monograph. This task is complicated because we also have to extricate material from his writings which reflects his ideas regarding the development of conversion symptoms in general. We will try to avoid the dangers of losing contexts in becoming interpreters rather than reviewers (1) by foregoing strict adherence to a historical sequence and (2) by grouping Freud's ideas relevant and coherent to the subsequent papers. This approach was found useful in the discussions of this workshop, and we hope will be found also here.

Before proceeding more specifically with Freud's concept of conversion as such, it might be more appropriate to indicate Freud's ideas about the relationships of physical and physiological processes. Two opinions he has held all his life. One was that there was no evidence of psychical processes occurring apart from physiological ones, and that no mental process could exist apart from a brain. The other was that physical processes must precede psychical ones, that is, information reaching the mind, whether from the outer world through the sense organs, or from the body through the chemical stimuli it provides, must begin as a physical excitation. Both opinions certainly would argue a priority for physiological processes. In one of his earliest papers (written with Breuer), "On the Theory of the Hysterical Attack" (1892), he attempted to integrate the empirical data of psychoanalytic psychology with neuroanatomy, neurophysiology and biophysics of his time. However, his first statement about correlated mind and brain activity is to be found in his book *On Aphasia* (1891), where he proclaimed himself an adherent of the doctrine of psychophysical parallelism. The problem of psyche-soma interrelation remained for some time in the center of his interest. When he finally (1910, 1923b) focused on the significance of psychoanalytic methodology for the study of psychic processes, he renounced the temptation to cross the boundary of psychophysiological research. He was only slightly interested in the first efforts of his pupils (Jelliffe, Groddeck, Felix Deutsch) to apply psychoanalysis to organically sick patients. In a letter to Viktor von Weizsaecker in 1923 (see Cremerius, 1957), he emphasized his awareness of the psychogenic factors in organic disease, but pointed out that because of didactic considerations the analyst should, for the time being, restrict himself to psychoanalytic research. A glimpse and a surmisal of this attitude is expressed in his study of "A Case of Obsessional Neurosis" (1909a), where he said in reference to the organic symptomatology, "Above all it does not involve the leap from a mental process to a somatic innervation—as in hysterical conversion, which can never be fully comprehensible to us."[1]

Until 1905, the year in which "Three Essays on the Theory of Sexuality" was published, Freud referred to the formation

[1] Ferenczi (1919) quoted Freud's "mysterious leap" from the mind to the soma in his article on hysterical materialization. Felix Deutsch (1924) used it in his paper "Some Reflections on the Formation of the Conversion Symptoms," read at the Seventh International Psychoanalytic Congress in Berlin in 1921.

of physical symptoms of psychogenic origin only in hysteria and anxiety neurosis. In both nosologic entities the process of symptom formation, as he pointed out (1905b), can be explained through unconscious defense mechanisms or regression. According to this concept, defense in hysteria is effected through conversion, and in anxiety neurosis through projection. This apparent difference is here especially pointed out because it has a bearing on the concept of conversion process as differentiated from Freud's understanding of the conversion symptom.[2] According to him, the hysterical symptom represents an experience which has been repressed and became unconscious, the symptom having been originally a constituent of the experience. Therefore, the motor phenomenon of the hysterical attack may in part be interpreted as general reaction phenomenon of the affect accompanying the memory. In anxiety neurosis symptoms merely represent the equivalent of a psychic condition. This differentiation is important in so far as it explains that in one case the sensory motor apparatus and organ systems are affected, while in the other those dependent on the vegetative nervous system become involved.

In Letter 18 to Fliess, Freud (1887-1902) states: "There is a kind of 'conversion' at work in anxiety neuroses just as there is in hysteria," indicating once again a similarity between the two.

In his discussion of Federn's case of an asthmatic attack (see Cremerius, 1957), Freud stated: "Sexual neuroses which have a psychic mechanism identical with that of hysteria, but which do not develop their symptoms through conversion, utilizing an abnormal somatic reaction instead, should be termed 'fixation hysteria' and regarded as a separate group of the anxiety and conversion hysterias." In Chapter 6 the role of preoedipal factors in conversion is considered in greater detail.

2 See Chapters 8 and 9.

Freud (1905b) expresses himself clearly in the following: "The theory does not by any means fail to point out that neuroses have an organic basis—though it is true that it does not look for that basis in any pathological anatomical changes, and provisionally substitutes the conception of organic functions for the chemical changes which we should expect to find but which we are at present unable to apprehend."

Freud introduced the term conversion in his first paper on the defense neuropsychoses (1894). A year later he used the concept in the discussion of his four cases of hysteria (Breuer and Freud, 1895), and elaborated and illustrated it further in the Case of Dora (1905b). He maintained that this concept was arrived at jointly with Breuer, although he admitted he was responsible for the word "conversion" himself (1914a). He said (1894), "I should like to propose the name of *conversion*[3] [to a process whereby] an unbearable idea is rendered innocuous by the quantity of excitation attached to it being transmuted into some bodily form of expression." He viewed this as part of a psychophysiological continuum when he stated (1909b): "A certain portion of our mental excitation is normally directed along the paths of somatic innervation and produces what we know as an 'expression of the emotions'," that is to say, that affects and emotions represent the awareness of discharge processes, implying discharge not only by an organic function such as salivation but also by hate or

[3] In his "History of the Psychoanalytic Movement" (1914a), Freud states: "Whenever Breuer, in his theoretical contribution to the *Studies on Hysteria* (1895), referred to this process of conversion, he always added my name in brackets after it, as though the priority for the first attempt at theoretical evaluation belonged to me. I believe that actually this distinction relates only to the name, and that the conception came to us simultaneously and together." Strachey comments: "There seems to be some mistake here. In the course of Breuer's contribution, he used the term 'conversion' (or its derivatives) at least fifteen times. But only once (the first time he uses it) does he add Freud's name in brackets. It seems possible that Freud saw some preliminary version of Breuer's manuscript and dissuaded him from adding his name more than once in the printed book." (See *Standard Edition*, Vol. XIV, p. 9, fn. 1.)

love, that is, both physiologically and psychologically at the same time.

Relevant to the discussion of conversion is Freud's hypothesis (1920) that there is an attempt on the part of the psychic apparatus "to keep the quantity of excitation present as low as possible or at least constant." The "principle of constancy"[4] dates back to Freud's earliest psychological cognition. It is discussed at length in the beginnings of his "Project for a Scientific Psychology" (1895) under the name of "the principle of neurotic inertia." Freud captured the importance of conversion in the following analogy (1909b): "When the bed of a stream is divided into two channels, then, if the current in one of them is brought up against an obstacle, the other will at once be overfilled. As you see, we are on the point of arriving at a purely psychological theory of hysteria, with affective processes in the front rank." Hysterical conversion exaggerates this portion of the discharge of an emotionally cathected mental process and represents a far more intense expression of the emotions which entered on a new path either in part or *in toto*. Later (1939) he described the ego function in regard to external events as the process of becoming aware of stimuli from without by storing up experiences of them in memory, by avoiding excess stimuli through flight, and by dealing with moderate stimuli through adaptation and finally by learning to bring about appropriate modification in the external world through activity.

Conversion proceeds along the line of the motor or sensory innervation and is more or less intimately related to the traumatic experience. These motor symptoms all can be

4 Strachey makes the following comments in his translation of Freud's *Beyond the Pleasure Principle*: "The first published discussion of it . . . was by Breuer . . . in his theoretical part of the *Studies on Hysteria* (1895). He there defines it as 'the tendency to keep intracerebral excitation constant.' In the same passage, he attributes this principle to Freud." (See *Standard Edition*, Vol. XVIII, p. 9, fn. 2.) Freud also refers to it in "A Letter to Joseph Breuer" (1892) and in his essay (with Breuer) "On the Theory of the Hysterical Attack" (1892).

shown to have an original or long-standing connection with traumata and are symbols for them in memory. The memory trace of the repressed idea is not annihilated by this process but forms the nucleus of a secondary psychical group. Hence, conversion is affected by the ego, which thereby frees itself from conflict at the price of being burdened by a memory symbol; the latter remains in the conscious either as a permanent motor innervation or as a recurrent hallucinatory sensation. According to Freud (1911a), these fantasies are endowed with psychic reality and constitute the real world the patients live in. This process does not play an independent role in the etiology of bodily symptoms; it is merely an intermediate stage in the process of symptom formation (Freud, 1916-1917) through which fantasies became attached to the repressed material. Impressions of a similar kind subsequently experienced furnish the weakened idea with fresh affect and re-establish for a time an associative character between the two psychical groups until a conversion creates a defense against it. A perpetual defense is going on against sexual ideas continuously arising anew, and these demonstrate an operation in process that has not yet been completed. As early as 1905, Freud refers to body-image problems by defining awareness of bodily organs predominantly disturbed by an image of the genitals leading to displacement. He referred to the "second wave of repression" of sensation from the clitoris, the "childhood penis" of girls, which they must have successfully accomplished before they can achieve vaginal orgasm (1905a).

In *Studies on Hysteria* (1895), from his observation of Frau Emmy von N., Freud concludes that an incomplete transformation, that is, conversion, is more usual than a complete one, so that part of the affect that accompanies the trauma persists in consciousness as a component of the subjective state of feeling reflected as such in alterations of mood, phobias, abulias, etc. In this case Freud demonstrates clearly the mechanism of conversion for the purpose of defense, pointing out that the erotic idea was repressed and the affect attached to that idea was used to intensify or revive the physical pain, which was present simultaneously or before the traumatic experience. In the case of Miss Lucy R. he discovered that before a hysteria can be acquired for the first time, one essential condition must be fulfilled, namely, that an idea must be intentionally excluded from consciousness and associative modification. This intentional repression is also a basic factor for the conversion—partial or total—representing the sum of excitation involved. Jones (1953) points out, apropos the case of Miss Lucy R., that the symptom turned out to be due to the repression of a forbidden wish in relation to her employer, enabling Freud to describe clearly how the active process of repressing an incompatible idea results in the substitution of a somatic innervation (conversion). In the case of Miss Lucy R., the advantage of conversion appeared to be that the incompatible idea is repressed from the ego's consciousness with amnesia for the important complex. The occurrence of several traumata and the preliminary latency of symptoms in Fräulein Elisabeth von R. led Freud to assume that conversion can result equally from recent symptoms as from recollected ones. That conversion does not always occur immediately after the trauma but also after an interval of incubation was demonstrated in the case of Katherina (Breuer and Freud, 1895).

In the case of Dora, Freud (1905b) brought together his conceptualization of the conversion process in the analytic situation. Dora, "merely a case of '*petite hystérie*' with the commonest of all somatic and mental symptoms: dyspnoea, *tussis nervosa*, aphonia, and possibly migraines, together with depression, hysterical unsociability, and a *taedium vitae* which was probably not entirely genuine," proved to be a most valuable clinical research subject. She provided the opportunity for Freud to consider the factors contributing to the development of the conversion symptom, as there are: heredity and constitution; the different psychic traumata, particularly the sexual trauma in childhood; the traumatic effect of the primal scene, then of pregnancy, childbirth, confinement, etc. He then mentions the modes of reaction formations: the reversal of affect, displacement of sensation, sensory hallucinations, derivations for feelings of disgust, the pathogenic significance of the comprehensive tie uniting the sexual and the excremental function. In addition, he emphasizes somatic compliance, the multiple meaning of symptoms, the role of bisexuality, the role of loss as well as the role of chance events. That sums up to the fact that the production of a hysterical conversion symptom "depends on the concurrence of many favourable conditions. The somatic compliance necessary for conversion is so seldom forthcoming, that an impulsion towards the discharge of an unconscious excitation will so far as possible make use of any channel for discharge which may already be in existence. It appears to be far more difficult to create a fresh conversion than to form paths of association between a new thought which is in need of discharge and the old one which is no longer in need of it. . . . the somatic side of a hysterical symptom is the more stable of the two and the harder to replace, while the psychical side is a variable element for which a substitution can more easily be found."

Identification mechanisms appear in different forms together with conversion mechanisms. On one occasion, for instance, it may appear as an "identification based on equal etiological claims" as demonstrated by Freud in the case of the boarding school girls who developed seizures after one of the girls had a seizure following the receipt of a love letter, in contravention of the rules of the school. This example is an impressive demonstration of the compromise formation of hysterical symptoms: the symptom expresses simultaneously gratification of the drive and punishment for it. Another form is that of identification with the lucky rival. Dora developed a cough similar to that of her unconscious rival, identifying with the rival in the somatic symptom instead of with the successful libidinal situation, thus expressing aspects of both guilt and punishment. Dora's throat complaint expressed the unconscious desire for fellatio, thus demonstrating the typical mechanism of displacement from below.

In his paper "From the History of an Infantile Neurosis" (1918), Freud points out that the conversion process may also involve the visceral organs. He continues in regard to an evaluation of the patient's condition: "It must be regarded as a true hysteria, showing not merely anxiety symptoms[5] but also phenomena of conversion. A portion of the homosexual impulses was retained by the organ concerned in it. From that time forward and equally during his adult life his bowel behaved like a hysterically affected organ." The unconscious repressed homosexuality withdrew into his bowel.

In his correspondence with Fliess (1887-1902), Freud mentioned his interest in the vicissitudes of the affects, especially as they become converted into organic symptoms. He points out that the child witnessing primal scenes during early childhood cannot yet sufficiently translate its impression and their memory traces into verbal images. He considered it of minor importance whether these scenes were observed in the period after the second dentition or during puberty, since patients with hysteria are always inclined to react with conversions, because the combined effect of defense and sexual impulses prevents verbal expression. The periods during

5 Based on his clinical observations, Freud expressed the opinion that in anxiety neuroses certain physical symptoms such as disturbance of the cardio-vascular system, profuse sweating, tremor, attacks of hunger, diarrhea, vertigo, vasomotor instability, paresthesias may be equivalents of the anxiety state and may in fact wholly substitute it. To the question as to why the nervous system should react to this "affective state," he replied that the psyche behaves as if it "projected the stimulus outward" and pointed out that the psyche and "the nervous system reacts in neuroses toward an internal source of excitation in the same way as to an analogous external one" (Freud, 1932).

which the events occur are less decisive, while the nature of the scenes is of importance in so far as it determines the degree of the defense. He stated that with great pathological endowment, even minor environmental traumata would lead to conversion symptoms. Thus he introduced by implication the genetic factor as a qualitative possibility, searching thereby for a correlation between certain types of neuroses and certain phases of libidinal development. In 1913 he arrived at the recognition of genetic factors in the choice of the neurosis and later in the development of the ego (1931-1937). Important for the understanding of symptom formation is further the manner in which defense mechanisms vary with the different stages of psychic development. It is conceivable, as he argues, that the psychic apparatus utilizes different methods prior to the clear-cut separation of ego and id and before the formation of a superego than it does after these stages of organization have been attained.

Freud regarded libido theory not only as an essential part of the theory of neuroses, but it also supported his initial concept of conversion symptom formation. This meant to him that in situations where failures of either an external or an internal nature occur, there is regression of the libido to an old fixation area at the erogenous zones or to objects of this earlier period. The organs or organ systems of the corresponding erogenous zones take on the functions of genitals, a fact which leads to disturbances in their function. Thus in voyeurism and exhibitionism the eye becomes erogenized; in masochism, the skin; in orality, the upper digestive tract; in sadism, the lower digestive tract. These organic disturbances are all masked forms of sexual gratification at the erogenous sites of those organ systems (Freud, 1908b, 1915d). For example, he states (1905a): "The retention of fecal matter, with the intention of using it as masturbatory stimulus of the anal zone is one of the most common causes of constipation. . . . Erogenous and hysterogenous zones display identical characteristics."

In Letter 75 to Fliess, Freud (1887-1902) for the first time puts the mechanisms of regression in the center of his dynamic explanation of the neuroses. In the same letter he developed the idea that the effect of a specific experience on the child's development is dependent on the stage of maturity it has reached. He said succinctly that "the choice of neurosis probably depends on the nature of the development which enables repression to occur." Freud's early emphasis on pathogenic id tendencies and on the modes of the id demands as the most important factors in symptom formation gradually gave way to his increased interest in the ego and its repressed forces, as well as in identification, as factors leading to symptom formation (1926).[6]

In his paper on the psychogenic disturbances of vision (1910), Freud conceptualizes that a neurosis can lead "through toxic modification" to structural changes, thus separating neurosis from psychogenic disturbances. Accordingly, these organic conditions have no definite psychic meaning but are the consequence of changes in physiological functions of the organs. He did not mean that these changes are not also influenced by unconscious motivations. It is implied that unconscious factors, as the symbolization of objects in the organs, also determine the functional activity of the organ. Freud (1909a) states: "Where an external stimulus becomes internal through harassing and destroying an organ, so that it results in an always new source of continuous excitation and in an increase of tension, it acquires a far-reaching similarity to an instinctual drive." The sexuality of these cases is predominantly pregenital, hence a source of extensive conflicts, giving rise to anxiety and to an upsurge of aggression. It is therefore difficult to qualify how far the somatic

[6] See Chapter 7 dealing with the role of identification in the conversion process.

manifestations are due to libidinal, aggressive, or anxiety factors. The external stimulus becomes internalized and adds to the primary instinctual drive. Hence, the instinctual drive becomes increased through what the external stimulus symbolizes.

In Draft K, Freud (1887-1902) states in regard to ego behavior in psychotics: "With the return of the repressed in a distorted form, the defence has failed; and the delusions of assimilation cannot be regarded as secondary defensive symptoms but must be interpreted as the beginning of a *modification of the ego,* an expression of the fact of its being overwhelmed. The process reaches its conclusion either in melancholia (a sense of littleness of the ego), which, in a secondary manner, attaches to the distortions the belief which has been withheld from the primary process, or—what is more frequent and more serious—it ends in the formation of *protective delusions* (megalomania), until the ego has been completely remodelled." During his study of the Schreber case (1911b), Freud's attention was drawn to the fact that ego drives are also of a libidinous nature, that is, sexual drives which are not directed toward external objects but toward the ego. Since in cases of hypochondria the organs are not demonstrably diseased, he conceived the idea that there might be certain organic changes necessary to release the process of libido withdrawal. In attempting to clarify the nature of these organic changes, he found a link connecting libido theory and the concept of narcissism (1914b). He described how partial drives recommence their strivings in an isolated manner, according to the pleasure principle, and how the various body areas, especially their erogenous zones, start to behave like sex organs. Hence, every erogenous fluctuation in relation to body organs may be paralleled by a change in the libido investment of the ego. Such processes have the same effect on libido distribution as an actual disease of the organs (1915d). In melancholia Freud observed the highest degree of withdrawal of object libido toward the ego, employed to form an identification of the ego with the relinquished object. Due to a simultaneous regression from object cathexis to the oral phase (the latter still belonging to narcissism), this identification assumes the character of introjection (1911b, 1915d, 1917). During this process different parts of the body as well as the function of its organs become progressively invested with libido. Since the mechanism of introjection belongs to the oral phase, the erogenicity and the libido are increased in the specific organ, as is its function (digestive system) through the withdrawal of libido from external objects.

Freud made the first reference to visible behavior in contrast to invisible behavior when he introduced the theory of two modes of cognition, the "primary processes" and the "secondary processes" (1900). Primary processes are an affective kind of cognition based on the pleasure principle. At this stage, the pleasurable sensations originate from sensory stimuli which are discharged in motor activity. Objects directly perceived or only remembered are essentially equivalent if their affective character is the same. Although Freud does not write it explicitly, it is implied that the pleasure-pain principle is the basis for the discharge in basic physiological, i.e., chemical and hormonal, processes. As soon as object awareness arises, the discharge continuum is altered by the process of introjection.

Freud deals with the problem of the conversion process as it manifests itself in the manner in which the dream treats auditory percepts (1900). He indicates that when verbal ideas appear as day residues of recent fragments of perception, they are handled like concrete ideas and become subject to the mechanism of condensation and displacement. He considered as the chief accomplishment of the dream work the transformation of the latent thoughts into perceptual formation, most commonly visual images (1916-1917). Hence thoughts originate from sensory percepts, and the first stages of their development consist of sensory impressions of their memory pictures. Later on, words are attached to these pictures and then connected so as to form thoughts. These observations imply that one cannot completely shut out external stimuli, that is, one can only repress perceptions whereby sensory impressions and memory pictures are fused with objects. Originally physiological sensory perceptions are then symbolized, and the symbols imbedded therein stimulate physiological processes leading to object images. This means that there is a revival of physiological processes for the purpose to recathect the related objects. This early form of percept is involved in what Freud (1900) referred to as the hallucinatory revival of the percept of the need-gratifying object. An essential component of the experience of the satisfaction of a need is a particular perception, the mnemic image, which remains associated with the memory trace of the excitation produced by the need. As a result of this link, each time the need arises a physical impulse emerges which seeks to recathect the mnemic percept of the image and to re-evoke the original satisfaction. An impulse of this kind is what we know as a wish. The reappearance of the percept is the fulfillment of the wish, and the shortest path to the fulfillment of the wish is a path leading directly from the excitation produced by the need to a complete cathexis of the percept. The first mnemic traces can be established only by an experience of gratification which interrupts the excitation arising from an internal need (Freud, 1900). This experience puts an end to the internal stimulus.

A special ego function develops which calls for a periodical search of the outer world in order that its data might be available and familiar in case an urgent inner instinctual need should arise. Its activity meets the sensory perception halfway instead of awaiting its appearance. This search of the outer world is stimulated by sensations in the body when reprojection has already taken place. The hyperirritability of organ systems and the heightening of thresholds is used for the expression of the need to find the desired object. The object may not be an extraneous one, as part of the subject's body may be utilized (1915d), and it may be changed any number of times in the course of the vicissitudes which the instinct undergoes during life.

Fundamentally, organic symptoms due to the conversion process may occur in all organs according to their erogenicity. Several determining factors for the choice of the organ and for fixation of the resulting symptomatology of a certain organic process need to be considered, such as somatic or psychic traumata, the aptness of certain organs for the symbolic expression of certain psychic conflicts, the qualifications of the defense mechanism, the timing and the purpose of the libido fixations, and the regressions therefrom. In addition, there exist multiple identifications in which the choice of the organ and of the symptom can be understood only after a more careful analysis of the details. The reference made here is to the history of the patient who wishes to strip herself of her clothes with the left hand while trying to hold onto them with the right. She thus identifies herself with the assaulting male as well as with the attacked female (Freud, 1908a).

There can be no libido development without the formation of fixations on earlier phases. Symptoms such as vomiting or disturbances in defecation may find their explanation through fixation on oral or anal spheres, due to transient regressive tendencies.

The withdrawal of libido from any likely real satisfaction and its overinvestment in fantasy raises the question as to how the libido could possibly find its way back to the point of original fixation. The objects and tendencies abandoned by the libido are not yet abandoned in every sense. Libido is being retained with variable degrees of intensity and fantasies. "Libido has therefore only to fall back upon the fantasies in order to find the way open to all repressed fixations" (Freud, 1916-1917). These fantasies represent at the same time leftovers of the pleasure principle which is herein able to pursue wish fulfillments with complete disregard of reality. The primary process prevails, condensation and displacement may take place, experiences and activities of infantile sexuality recur. Partial drives and objects which had been abandoned in childhood are resurrected. Traumatic experiences, incidents which took place in childhood attach themselves to these drives. Above all, they become fused with the infantile fantasies of seduction, observation of parental intercourse and castration. Along with the regression to the pleasure principle, there also exists a regression to a form of heightened autoerotism. The perceptual changes of the external world are replaced by changes in the perception of the body, that is, an internal action replaces the external one.

According to Freud (1911a), these fantasies are endowed with psychic reality and constitute the real world the patient lives in. This process does not play an independent role in the etiology of body symptoms. It is only "an intermediate stage in the process of symptom formation through which fantasies become attached to repressed material" (1916-1917). Freud observed a similar process of object-libido withdrawal in a transference neurosis; however, in contrast to the narcissistic neurosis, object-libido withdrawal occurred without abolishment of object cathexis, because in a transference neurosis libido cannot be withdrawn from the object when a person has reached the genital stage of development.

Since Freud conceptualized that in a compulsion neurosis the regression of libido to the anal-sadistic phase takes place only after the phallic phase has been reached, it is conceivable that organic symptoms in compulsion neurosis originate in the same manner as in hysteria (1926). They are composites of functional bodily disorders on different levels. All sensory perceptions are then forerunners of motoric actions which the ego uses to protect itself against imagined dangers (1938). Visual, olfactory, and auditory percepts keep the object away. Kinesthetic or taste or touch sensations let the object come nearer and accept it to a certain extent. The resulting kinesthetic sensation mediates the movement of the perceived imagined object into different distances. Hypersensitivity can be used as a defense against the danger of other specific sensory sensations. Pain can either be a tactile sensation due to the contact with the tabooed imagined object which executes the punishment, and/or the pleasure gratification as a result of this contact. Therefore the sensitivity to real organic pain depends also on the need for the punishment, for the contact with the tabooed imagined objects. This concept permits the conclusion that the ego alters the function of an organ when its erogenicity and its sexual significance increase: "The ego impairs the appropriate functions in order to avoid a renewed repression so as not to come into conflict with the id" (Freud, 1926).

In visual disturbances of psychogenic origin, the ego acts according to the law of talion and punishes the eroticized organ, the eye, by denying it the ability to see. "You wanted to misuse your visual organ in order to gratify your sinful lust. Therefore it serves you right that you cannot see at all" (Freud, 1910). However, the ego has also to avoid a conflict with the superego and is feigning to carry out actions which may appear successful and may be to its advantage.

The role of the various sensory perceptions in the conversion process can be deduced from Freud's assumption (1923c) that the superego develops from the sensory crust of the id, especially the so-called *"Hörkappe"* (auditory lobe), which is turned toward the environment. In this respect, the auditory sphere occupies, according to Freud, an exceptional position which is of greater importance than the other sensory organs. Just as the body ego is the nucleus of the ego, the human auditory sphere as adapted in the direction of a capacity for language is to be regarded as the nucleus of the superego. The function of the ego (1916-1917) is not limited to external perception but includes internal perception as well. Speaking about the origin of flying in dreams (1900) and of how sexual excitation in dreams is produced (1905a), Freud hypothesizes that the latter originates from rhythmic mechanical agitation of the body which operates on the vestibular nerves, on the skin, on the muscles and articular structures. Thereby he explains how a psychic phenomenon like a dream develops from a physiological stimulus which acts as a psychic stimulus at the same time.

Freud (1909a) traced the origin of repression of sensory perceptions to their sexualization. Hence hypersensitivity to smell and odors is due to repression of tabooed awareness of the genitals. If visual perception of the sex organs is repressed, the olfactory sensations take over the scotomized vision of the organs. Thus olfactory sense perception may become repressed like the visual perception. The result may be the development of a hyposensitive olfactory function, that is, the threshold becomes lowered. Repression of anal erotism leads to olfactory sensory repression; so organic functions representing tabooed thoughts are repressed, that is, transformations of mind processes into organic ones are effected. In the Rat Man (1909a), Freud brought a clinical example of the transition from a pregenitally tabooed recognition of genitals, which was expressed in the patient's hypersensitivity to odors. He was a *renifleur*, and by his own account recognized as a child everyone by their smell. Even when he was grown up, he remained sensitized to odors. In the analytic session the internalized object becomes conscious through sensations of smell, imagined or real—referred to as coming from outside.

These and similar conversion symptoms represent permanent or intermittent cathected physiological processes and are replacements of repressed infantile sexual drives from their associative connection with the latter. The symptoms themselves are only parts of a basic complex. One therefore comes to the conclusion that when infantile sexual energy becomes displaced, it appears converted and concentrated on a limited area of the entire complex. From this point of view, motor paralysis is a form of defense against a certain action which should have been carried out in the given situation but which has been repressed (1926). It is an essential presupposition for such a conversion that the sense of reality is diminished on account of the repression and of the fantasies in which the real sexual object is replaced by imaginary substitutions of infantile objects.

While Freud laid the foundations of psychoanalysis on the basis of observations of patients with hysteria, he never fully investigated the role of pregenitality and ego development in problems of hysteria. He alludes to this in *Inhibition, Symptom and Anxiety* (1926) and in his *New Introductory Lectures* (1932). Fenichel (1945) tried to fill some of this gap by introducing the term "pregenital conversion," as Deutsch had already proposed in 1924 (see Chapter 5). Fenichel claimed that conversion symptoms are not limited to the voluntary muscular systems but occur as well in the realm of the vegetative system. He felt that not all somatic changes of a psychogenic nature should be called conversion because not all were translations of specific fantasies into a "body language." He thought that unconscious instinctual attitudes may influence organic functions in a psychological way, also without the changes having any definite psychic meaning. Using asthma as an example, he postulated that apart from purely somatic factors, pregenital conversions determine this condition. He comments that the role played by the pregenital fixation may be limited to the organ that becomes the seat of the symptoms. This suggests that the concept of the conversion symptom should be broadened to include pregenitality as an important factor in the development of conversion symptoms.

Summary. We tried to cull from Freud's writings his basic views pertinent to the conversion process. This survey aims at serving as background for other chapters in this monograph. We recognize the shortcomings inherent in such an arbitrary selection, though appropriate for this purpose. At the same time we wished to illustrate how Freud paved the way for solving the problem of the "mystery of the leap from the mind to the body."

Part II

FELIX DEUTSCH:

From this review it can be recognized that Freud's concept of the conversion process stemmed from clinical observations for which the "Notes upon a Case of Obsessional Neurosis" (1909a) and the "Fragment of an Analysis of a Case of Hysteria" (1905b) were paradigmatic. They contain the clinical data which led Freud to introduce the term "conversion" into analysis, as well as the reasons why he restricted the use of this term to the conversion hysteria.

On two occasions I had the opportunity to bring to Freud's attention the possibility of broadening this concept beyond its original meaning. The first one occurred when I read a paper "On the Formation of the Conversion Symptom" (see Chapter 5) at one of the last meetings of the International Psychoanalytic Association which Freud attended (1922). The second one occurred when I shortly thereafter mentioned to him that I had seen Dora in consultation, twenty-three years after she had interrupted her analytic treatment.

The clinical observations and the theoretical considerations contained in the paper on the conversion symptom are of sufficient interest, at least historically, to be reprinted now, passing over from the past to the present to see where new conceptualizations and clinical observations may throw more light on the "mysterious leap."

On both occasions mentioned above it dawned on me that Freud's concept of conversion would become the bridge leading to shores where the fusion of bodily and mental processes may once be found. The follow-up of the events in Dora's life, as they were reported at the workshop, are a reminder that it needed Freud's genius, his new conceptualizations, to open new avenues for the investigators of the human mind.

4.

A FOOTNOTE TO FREUD'S "FRAGMENT OF AN ANALYSIS OF A CASE OF HYSTERIA"[1]

FELIX DEUTSCH, M.D.

In his biography of Freud, Ernest Jones refers to the well-known case of Dora (Freud, 1905b) and to her various hysterical somatic and mental symptoms. After stating that she never resumed her analysis of only eleven weeks' duration, he mentions that she "died a few years ago in New York" (Jones, 1955, p. 289).

For several reasons this fact aroused my interest. What did she die from? Could Freud's intuition and penetrating interpretation of only two dreams really bring to light the personality structure of this unfortunate girl? If he was right, should not the course of her later life bear out Freud's views of the various motives for retaining her conversion symptoms? And last but not least, how much further advanced are we today in understanding the "leap from the mental into the physiological"?

My particular curiosity about Dora's later life would have met an insurmountable obstacle from the beginning during Freud's life because of his discretion. He wrote: "I have waited for four whole years since the end of the treatment

[1] Reprinted from the *Psychoanalytic Quarterly*, 26:159-167, 1957.

and have postponed publication till hearing that a change
has taken place in the patient's life of such a character as
allows me to suppose that her own interest in the occurrences
and psychological events which are to be related here may
now have grown faint. Needless to say, I have allowed no
name to stand which could put a non-medical reader upon
the scent; and the publication of the case in a purely scientific and technical periodical should, further, afford a guaran-
tee against unauthorized readers of this sort. I naturally cannot prevent the patient herself from being pained if her own
case history should accidentally fall into her hands. But she
will learn nothing from it that she does not already know;
and she may ask herself who besides her could discover from
it that she is the subject of this paper."

Twenty-four years after Freud's treatment of Dora, an
event took place which dispelled the anonymity of this case
to another analyst without Freud's knowledge.

In a footnote added in 1923 to "Fragment of an Analysis
of a Case of Hysteria," Freud wrote: "The problem of medical discretion which I have discussed in this preface does not
touch the remaining case histories contained in this volume;
for three of them were published with the express assent of
the patients (or rather, as regards little Hans, with that of
his father), while in the fourth case (that of Schreber) the
subject of the analysis was not actually a person but a book
produced by him. In Dora's case the secret was kept until
this year. I had long been out of touch with her, but a short
while ago I heard that she had recently fallen ill again from
other causes, and had confided to her physician that she had
been analysed by me when she was a girl. This disclosure
made it easy for my well-informed colleague to recognize her
as the Dora of 1899. No fair judge of analytic therapy will
make it a reproach that the three months' treatment she received at that time effected no more than the relief of her

current conflict and was unable to give her protection against subsequent illnesses."

Freud withheld the name of the consulting physician in agreement with him, since it might have led to the disclosure of the patient's identity. Now that Dora is no longer alive, it can be revealed, without transgressing that discretion which protected her anonymity, why the note in Jones's book about Dora's death aroused my special interest. The reason is that I am the physician who told Freud in 1922 of my encounter with Dora. It happened shortly after the presentation of my paper, "On the Formation of the Conversion Symptom" (see Chapter 5) at the Seventh International Psychoanalytic Congress in Berlin, in September 1922, the last which Freud attended. I referred to some of the viewpoints raised in that paper and to the mysterious "leap from the mind to the soma," when I told Freud how my encounter with Dora took place and how I had *nolens volens* been let into the secret.

In the late fall of 1922, an otolaryngologist asked my opinion about a patient of his, a married woman, forty-two years old, who for some time had been bedridden with marked symptoms of Ménière's syndrome: tinnitus, decreased hearing in the right ear, dizziness, and sleeplessness because of continual noises in this ear. Since an examination of the inner ear, of the nervous system, as well as of the vascular system, showed no pathology whatever, he inquired whether a psychiatric study of the patient, who behaved very "nervously," might perhaps explain her condition.

The interview began in the presence of her physician. Her husband left the room shortly after he had listened to her complaints, and did not return. She started with a detailed description of the unbearable noises in her right ear and of dizziness when moving her head. She had always suffered from periodic attacks of migraine on the right side of her head. The patient then started a tirade about her husband's indifference toward her sufferings, and how unfortunate her marital life had been. Now her only son had also begun to neglect her. He had recently finished college and had to decide whether he should continue with his studies. However, he often stayed out late at night and she suspected he had become interested in girls. She always waited, listening, until he came home. This led her to talk about her own frustrated love life and her frigidity. Another pregnancy had appeared to her to be impossible because she could not endure the labor pains.

Resentfully she expressed her conviction that her husband had been unfaithful to her, that she had considered divorce, but could not decide what to do. Tearfully she denounced men in general as selfish, demanding, and ungiving. That brought her back to her past. She recalled with great feeling how close she had always been to her brother who had become the leader of a political party and who still visited whenever she needed him—in contrast to her father who had been unfaithful even to her mother. She reproached her father for having once had an affair with a young married woman whom she, the patient, had befriended, and whose children had been for some time under her care when she was a young girl. The husband of this woman had then made sexual advances to her which she had rejected.

This story sounded familiar to me. My surmise about the identity of the patient was soon confirmed. In the meantime, the otologist had left the room. The patient then began to chat in a flirtatious manner, inquiring whether I was an analyst and whether I knew Professor Freud. I asked her in turn whether she knew him and whether he had ever treated her. As if having waited for this cue, she quickly replied that she was the Dora case, adding that she had not seen a psychiatrist since her treatment with Freud. My familiarity with Freud's writings evidently created a very favorable transference situation.

She forgot to talk about her sickness, displaying great pride in having been written up as a famous case in psychiatric literature. Then she spoke of the failing health of her father who now often seemed out of his mind. Her mother had recently been admitted to a sanitarium to be treated for tuberculosis. She suspected that her mother might have acquired the tuberculosis from her father who, as she remembered, had this disease when he was a child. She apparently had forgotten her father's history of syphilis, mentioned by Freud, and which he considered in general a constitutional predisposition and a "very relevant factor in the etiology of the neuropathic constitution in children." She also expressed concern about her occasional colds and difficulties in breathing, as well as her coughing spells in the morning which she thought were due to her excessive smoking during past years. As if wanting to make this more acceptable, she said her brother had the same habit, too.

When I asked her to leave the bed and to walk around, she walked with a slight limp of the right leg. Questioned about the limp she could give no explanation. She had had it since childhood, but it was not always noticeable. Then she discussed Freud's interpretation of her two dreams, and asked my opinion about it. When I ventured to connect her Ménière's syndrome with her relationship to her son and with her continual listening for his return from his nightly excursions, she appeared ready to accept it, and asked for another consultation with me.

The next time I saw her she was out of bed and claimed that her "attacks" were over. The Ménière's symptoms had disappeared. Again she released a great amount of hostile feeling toward her husband, especially her disgust with marital life. She described her premenstrual pains and a vaginal discharge after menstruation. Then she talked mainly about her relationship to her mother, of her unhappy childhood because of her mother's exaggerated cleanliness, her annoying washing compulsions, and her lack of affection for her. Mother's only concern had been her own constipation from which the patient herself now suffered. She finally spoke with pride about her brother's career, but she had little hope that her son would follow in his footsteps. When I left her, she thanked me eloquently and promised to call me if she should feel the need. I never heard from her again. Her brother called several times shortly after my contact with his sister, expressing his satisfaction with her speedy recovery. He was greatly concerned about her continual suffering and her discord with both her husband and their mother. He admitted it was difficult to get along with her because she distrusted people and attempted to turn them against each other. He wanted to see me at my office, but I declined in view of Dora's improvement.

One can easily understand that this experience made me want to compare the clinical picture of the patient with the one Freud had described in his brief analysis twenty-four years earlier when she was eighteen years old. It is striking that Dora's fate took the course Freud had predicted. He admitted that "the treatment of the case and consequently my insight into the complex of events composing it, remained fragmentary. There are therefore many questions to which I have no solution to offer, or in which I can only rely upon hints and conjectures." These considerations, however, did not alter his basic concept that "the majority of hysterical symptoms, when they have attained their full pitch of development, represent an imagined situation of sexual life." Unquestionably Dora's attitude toward marital life, her frigidity and her disgust with heterosexuality, bore out Freud's concept of displacement which he described in these terms: "I can arrive at the following derivation for the feelings of disgust. Such feelings seem originally to be a reaction to the *smell* (and afterwards also to the *sight*) of excrement.

But the genitals can act as a reminder of the excremental functions."

Freud corroborated this concept later in his "Notes upon a Case of Obsessional Neurosis" (1909a), referring to the patient as a *renifleur* (osphresiolagniac), being more susceptible to sensations of smell than most people. Freud adds in a footnote that the patient "in his childhood had been subject to strong coprophilic propensities. In this connection his *anal erotism* has already been noticed."

We may ask, apart from the senses of *smell, taste,* and *vision,* whether other propensities for the use of *sensory* perception were involved in the conversion process of Dora. Certainly the *auditory* apparatus played an important role in the Ménière's syndrome. In fact, Freud refers to Dora's dyspnea as apparently conditioned by her listening as a child to the noises in her parents' bedroom which had then adjoined her own. This "listening" was repeated in her alertness for the sound of her son's footsteps when he returned home at night after she suspected he had become interested in girls.

As for her sense of *touch,* she had shown its repression in her contact with Mr. K., when he embraced her, and when she behaved as if she had not noticed the contact with his genitals. She could not deny the contact of her lips when Mr. K. kissed her, but she *defended* herself against the effect of this kiss by denying her own sexual excitement and her awareness of Mr. K.'s genitals, which she rejected with disgust.

We must remember that in 1894, Freud proposed the name "conversion" as a *defense,* when he arrived at the concept that "in hysteria the unbearable idea is rendered innocuous by the quantity of excitation attached to it being transmuted into some bodily form of expression." Even earlier, in collaboration with Breuer (1892), he phrased it: "The increase of the sum of excitation takes place along sensory paths and its diminution along motor ones. . . . If, however, there is no reaction whatever to a physical trauma, the memory of it retains the affect which it originally had." That still holds true today.

Many years went by during which Dora's ego continued in dire need of warding off her feelings of guilt. We learn that she tried to achieve it by an identification with her mother who suffered from a "housewife's psychosis" consisting of obsessional washing and other kinds of excessive cleanliness. Dora resembled her not only physically but also in this respect. She and her mother saw the dirt not only in their surroundings, but also on and within themselves. Both suffered from genital discharges at the time Freud treated Dora, as well as when I saw her.

It is striking that the dragging of her foot, which Freud had observed when the patient was a girl of eighteen, should have persisted twenty-five years. Freud stated that "a symptom of this kind can only arise when it has an infantile prototype." Dora had once twisted this foot when she was a child, slipping on a step as she was going downstairs. The foot had swelled, was bandaged, and she was kept in bed some weeks. It appears that such a symptom may persist through life, whenever there is a need to use it for the somatic expression of displeasure. Freud always adhered to "the concept of the biological rules" and considered displeasure "as being stored up for their protection. The somatic compliance, organically predetermined, paves the way for the discharge of an unconscious excitation."

The truth of Freud's statement, that "it appears to be far more difficult to create a fresh conversion than to form paths of association between a new thought which is in need of discharge and the old one which is no longer in need of it," cannot be overemphasized. The somewhat fatalistic conclusion which one might draw from Dora's personality, which twenty-five years later was manifested as Freud had seen and foreseen it, is that she could not escape her destiny. However, this statement needs some qualification. Freud himself states very clearly that he had not published the case "to put the value of psychoanalytic therapy in its true light" and that the briefness of the treatment (which hardly lasted three months) was only one of the reasons which prevented a longer lasting improvement of Dora's condition. Even if Freud had already made at that time his discoveries about transference neurosis and working through, Dora could not have benefited from them because she broke off the treatment unexpectedly as "an unmistakable act of vengeance on her part. Her purpose of self-injury also profited by this action."

More than thirty years have elapsed since my visit at Dora's sickbed. I would never have known anything more had Jones's note of her death in New York not helped me obtain further information concerning her later life. From my informant I learned the additional pertinent facts about the fate of Dora and of her family recorded here.

Her son brought her from France to the United States. Contrary to her expectations, he succeeded in life as a renowned musician. She clung to him with the same reproachful demands she made on her husband, who had died of a coronary disease—slighted and tortured by her almost paranoid behavior. Strangely enough, he had preferred to die, as my informant put it, rather than to divorce her. Without question, only a man of this type could have been chosen by Dora for a husband. At the time of her analytic treatment she had stated unequivocally: "Men are all so detestable that I would rather not marry. This is my revenge." Thus her marriage had served only to cover up her distaste of men.

Both she and her husband had been driven out of Vienna during World War II and emigrated initially to France. Before that she had been repeatedly treated for her wellknown attacks of hemicranial migraine, coughing spells, and hoarseness, which Freud had analytically interpreted when she was eighteen years old.

In the early thirties, after her father's death, she began to suffer from palpitations of the heart, which were thought to be caused by her excessive smoking. She reacted to these sensations with anxiety attacks and fear of death. This ailment kept everyone in her environment in continual alarm, and she utilized it to play off friends and relatives against each other. Her brother, also a "chain smoker," died much later from coronary disease in Paris where he had escaped under the most adventurous circumstances. He was buried there with the highest honors.

Dora's mother died of tuberculosis in a sanitarium. I learned from my informant that she had had the disease in her youth. She worked herself to death by her never-ending, daily cleaning compulsion—a task which nobody else could fulfill to her satisfaction. Dora followed in her footsteps, but directed the compulsion mainly to her own body. As her vaginal discharge persisted, she had several minor gynecological operations. The inability to "clean out her bowels," her constipation, remained a problem to the end of her life. Being accustomed to this trouble with her bowels, she apparently treated it as a familiar symptom until it became more than a conversion symptom. Her death from a cancer of the colon, which was diagnosed too late for a successful operation, seemed a blessing to those who were close to her. She had been, as my informant phrased it, "one of the most repulsive hysterics" he had ever met.

The additional facts about Dora presented here are no more than a footnote to Freud's postscript. But it may now stimulate reappraisal and discussion of the degree to which the concept of the process of conversion, in the sense Freud used it, is still valid, or in what respects it differs from our present-day comprehension of it.

5.

ON THE FORMATION OF THE
CONVERSION SYMPTOM[1]

FELIX DEUTSCH, M.D.

The concept of the conversion process is now gaining in importance because similar transformation processes from psychic into organic phenomena can be observed also in diseases which by no means appeared to be psychogenic ones. Indeed, these conditions were evidenced in patients whose organic symptoms were unequivocally of a functional nature, but occurred within an organic illness. Thus Freud's concept of "conversion" may be carried beyond its original meaning. Observations on the medical ward fully justify the broadening of this term.

Psychological exploration of organic diseases from this standpoint discovers in the organic symptomatology so many psychic components and brings to the fore such significant signposts of the repressed unconscious which seemed to have played a role in the development of organic diseases, that the "leap from the psychic into the organic" becomes less mysterious.

If it could be proved that purely organic symptoms can be ameliorated through analytic treatment just as functional

[1] Paper read at the Seventh International Psychoanalytical Congress in Berlin, September 1922, first published in *Internationale Zeitschrift für Psychoanalyse*, 10:380-392, 1924.

disturbances are removed when repressions are lifted, then the intermediary pathways of the conversion process which lead to the organic symptoms could be clarified. It has to be admitted that a medical man has a greater interest in investigating these mechanisms than the analyst, because analysis proper cannot anticipate greater contributions from the psychologic point of view. Nevertheless, it seems important to trace the interplay of psychic and physiologic factors to their deepest amalgamation.

It has clearly been established that organic manifestations can be the result of repressed unconscious conflicts. Hence the borders between the psychic and the organic become indistinguishable. A considerable part of organic symptomatology will then be recognized as the result of the conversion process.

For this reason the specific organic cause of a disease will have to share its importance for symptom formation with certain psychic factors, because they have for some time been latently present in the total functioning of the organism, before the psychophysiologic breakdown occurs. A thorough psychic exploration of organically sick persons always shows that the subjective awareness of being sick coincides with an emotional experience, which by its coincidence determines the course of the sickness. The symptomatology of organic diseases always contains a series of sensorimotor manifestations which are interspersed in the sum total of organic symptoms and which as a rule are regarded as insignificant by-products. However, these symptoms are not only concomitants of the disease, they have their latent psychic predetermination. Perhaps with the exception of the infectious diseases or bodily injuries through accidents, all illnesses are subject to the principle of psychophysiologic determination. This statement refers not only to the so-called organic compliance in organ neuroses. By and large, the choice of the avenues of discharge in the autonomic system, whether it is nausea, or perspiration, or headache, or diarrhea, or tachycardia, will depend on how far the psychologic process has progressed.

The specific organic symptoms constituting the disease are either repetitions of previous dysfunctions which formerly had been unrecognized conversions and which were abandoned when they had lost their usefulness for the expression of the unconscious—or they reappeared because of the accidental organic disease in a highly cathected organ system which had been conditioned for the development of a conversion symptom for a long time, thus closing the cycle which preceded its appearance. As in organic chemistry, where atoms unite to form chains of more or less complexity to build a specific chemical compound, a specific amalgamation between psychic and physical factors is necessary for the development of a conversion symptom.

The following observations illustrate how a conversion symptom comes into being, thereby revealing the psychic determinants which gradually lead to the organic symptomatology. They demonstrate how the conversion symptom originates from an inevitable transformation process from the psychic into the organic, and that this process does not occur suddenly, but develops gradually.

A middle-aged male patient, a physician, complained that he could scarcely walk because of severe pain in his right foot of one year's duration. The foot had suddenly felt like dead. The attending surgeon made the diagnosis of an occlusion of a foot artery, and even considered amputation of the foot. The latter could be avoided, however, when the circulation in the foot artery improved considerably, apparently through collateral pathways. But in spite of it, all subsequent therapeutic procedures brought only temporary relief of the intermittent pain. After all attempts to relieve what was obviously a claudicatio intermittens had failed, the patient thought that his nervous condition might contribute to his physical disability and he asked for advice. He recalled that his symptoms started on the day of a severe emotional upset. Soon after leaving the hospital where his little nephew had just died, he suffered the first painful attack in his foot.

The physical examination of this forty-year-old man corroborated his statements. The pulse of his right foot artery (Art. dors. ped.) was not palpable, the foot being cooler than the left. No arteriosclerotic vascular changes could be found. Since the medical treatment had not brought relief of his pain, the patient was accepted for analytic treatment. The analysis which led to the disappearance of his symptoms yielded pertinent information concerning the psychic motivation of the organic symptom.[2]

Analysis does not deal with the symptoms as such, but with the underlying unconscious meaning. The pain could to a great extent, though not fully, be explained by the insufficient blood circulation. However, the following questions remained: what role did the right foot play in the mind of the patient, and how far could its meaning contribute to the painful sensation? In other words, had a conversion from the psychic into the organic occurred?

In brief, the following unconscious determinants of the symptom could be established. The patient's difficulty in walking appeared to be an unconscious expression of his sexual impotency. "I can't do it—I can't walk." He had to stop suddenly in the street to lace his shoe tighter, because he had a feeling as if his foot were "hanging loosely" in the shoe. Thus the foot served as a phallic symbol. The walking difficulty began on the day when his nephew died, the son of his brother whom he envied for his potency. Furthermore, the funeral prevented him from keeping a date with a woman

[2] Freud referred indirectly to this case, when he wrote: "Some analysts (Jelliffe, Groddeck, Felix Deutsch) have reported that the analytic treatment of gross organic diseases is not unpromising, since a mental factor not infrequently contributes to the origin and continuance of such illnesses" (1923b, p. 125).

with whom he had had an affair and with whom he had proved to be potent. He felt frustrated and—the foot denied him its service. At the same time, he punished himself for his death wish toward the boy.

From then on, he walked with a conspicuous limp. He developed a compulsion to touch with that foot scraps of paper and other litter on his way, as if he wanted to examine their "mysterious" content. This resulted in a slightly stumbling gait. Furthermore, the "mystery" of his walking difficulties could be interpreted as follows: almost fifteen years ago, as a student, he had read in a medical textbook that "claudicatio intermittens is a most mysterious disease." From then on, this statement stuck in his mind. He became interested in patients with this disease and he examined them with a certain curiosity. Simultaneously with his concern about his impotence, his interest in the circulation of his *dorsalis pedis* led to a compulsive testing of the pulse of his artery.

However, the "mystery" had deeper determinants. His unconscious incestuous wishes toward his mother had called for repressive tendencies, with the result that he retained the notion of a "mysterious" female genital. Although he was a physician, his knowledge of female anatomy remained vague. A further unconscious motivation for his limping was that his mother always walked with a slight limp, which he had often tried to imitate, acting out in this way his identification with her. For that reason he paid particular attention to his gait ever since he was a child. Finally, the choice of limping as a conversion symptom appeared to be based on an event in the patient's childhood. As a little boy he had once put his right foot mischievously in his mother's way when she walked through the room, and she really fell down. It was this foot which now troubled him. This memory relived in the analysis evoked a great amount of guilt feeling. The need to punish the foot which committed the crime is evident. All these highly charged unconscious conflicts prepared his mind for the development of the conversion symptom involving the foot.

In general I would postulate that the conversion process can lead to a "conversion symptom" only when many well-defined psychic components coincide most suitably with an organic disorder. The relationship between psychic and organic determinants is interlinked, similar to that of two communicating tubes. If the level in one goes down, it goes up in the other.

In applying this concept to the symptoms of this patient, we are cognizant that he limped because of the pain due to the partly occluded foot artery as well as due to his inner need to express his unconscious conflicts. Still, the question remains, how the mysterious leap from the mind to the soma took place. Is it possible that a vascular system reacts to the needs of the unconscious in such a specific and selective way? Is such an assumption defendable or is it unjustified to bring the acute psychic trauma and the conversion symptom in too close an etiological relationship? In any case, the fact remains that long-lasting psychic processes are necessary before a conversion symptom can develop.

In the case presented here an organic vascular process could be suspected since the patient had been treated for syphilis about twenty years ago. However, there was no evidence in the vascular system of a possible aftereffect of the syphilis before the claudicatio began. Nevertheless, it is possible that independent of the disease, a vasomotor neurosis had been present before.

It is known that syphilis is very often accompanied or followed by an increase of the blood eosinophilia. The same occurrence has been observed in neurotic conditions without sufficient explanation up to now. In this case a considerable eosinophilia was found. One can argue whether it was caused by the neurotic or by the organic process. It is also possible that the blood eosinophilia, which was originally due to syphilis, was later caused by the conversion process. The latter explanation is far more plausible, because the eosinophilia—during the analysis and without any other treatment —gradually decreased to normal, even before the claudicatio ceased. This fact suggests that the increase of the eosinophiles was due to the conversion process.

With some reservations we may conclude that in this case the organic matrix has gradually become infiltrated by the conversion process which influenced the vasomotor function until the conversion symptom became established. Disregarding some unknown psychophysiologic factors, the "mystery" of the conversion process disappeared to some extent.

Similar observations can very likely be made in most functional organic disorders. This became evident to me in the analysis of a patient with gall-bladder colics, in a case with intermittent achylia, and in a patient with diabetes insipidus. These observations convinced me that the conversion symptoms are organic manifestations of a psychophysiologic process which operated in a hidden form over a long time, and that they had been transformed into a specific symptom complex through a psychophysiologic occurrence. The pathways which finally lead to the symptom formation are well defined. The psychophysiologic process is active long before a conversion symptom is established, but its various preparatory steps are difficult to follow and can be validated only in analysis.

It must be assumed that a continuous conversion process, necessary for the maintenance of health and well-being, takes place in every normal individual. Let us think, for instance, of blushing, of excessive perspiration, of spells of diarrhea, of attacks of migraine, of the manifold motility behaviors which are maintained and stabilized through repetition and practice, and which characterize the individual. They all occur only as discharges of pent-up libido and of the emotional debris which through its accumulation burdens the unconscious. The concept of conversion has to be broadened to encompass such reactive patterns. However, the hysterical conversion symptom still retains its particular significance. Compared with the "conversions" of normal individuals, it differs in so far as its development is based on a constitutional or predispositional inability to ward off emotional tensions which the healthy individual masters without apparent difficulty, but which in the hysterical individual lead to an inevitable transformation of great amounts of libido into organic manifestations.

Of course, this pressing need is absent in the normal individual. Nevertheless, it is possible that some previous organic change, or the psychic cathexis of an organ brought about by special circumstances, may induce even the non-hysterical individual to convert the ever-present, pent-up and repressed affects in that organ system.

To a certain extent, "conversions" are necessary forms of a continual psychodynamic process which attempts to adjust the individual's instinctual drives to the demands of the culture in which he lives. Their most suitable targets are body parts with an organic pathology. If such changes are not present, these organ systems are used for transitory conversions according to their symbolic suitability. *One might say that human beings would be most unhappy or would take far more flight into a neurosis if they could not fall sick* from time to time. For it is during periods of sickness that the conversion process finds an inconspicuous outlet, which is barred at other times. In other words, the more violently the conversion breaks through during a sickness, the more serious will be its course.

Although the clinical observations referred to above suffice to make the conversion process appear somewhat less mysterious, one must admit that they do not reveal the roots of the transition of the psychic into the organic. An attempt to pursue these sources further certainly approaches a purely biological, or rather a metabiological, problem. It will lead to the borders of three scientific disciplines. In fact, all three of them have already made attempts to tackle this problem. But so far neither the biology of the organic, nor the philosophy of the organic, nor the psychology of the organic have succeeded in finding a satisfactory explanation. This is either due to the inadequacy of our scientific methods, or to the fact that we are here dealing with incommensurable factors. In any case, one can speculate that one approach to the problem might start with the most simple cell processes.

When two germ cells are fused, an energetic mutual effect of the nucleus and protoplasm upon another results, followed by chemical changes in the protoplasmic properties of these cells. It has been objectively proved that an interaction of the chemical properties of the nuclear and the germ plasm of the two cells is set in motion. This simplest form of stimulation is noticeable through movement. Both the movement and the energy transfer are terminated when the physicochemical stimulation of the cells upon another ceases. Certain parts of the nucleus produce those chemical products which lead to alterations of the cytoplasm, constantly creating new chemical properties, whereby the changed protein qualities of the protoplasm act on the nuclear plasm.

If this endogenous physicochemical process remained undisturbed by extraneous factors, the cycle of organic development would always take the same course until the individual —be it the lowest or the most highly developed living unit— has reached maturity. Furthermore, on account of cell activities due to the cell's memory (Hering's *Seele*) which contains inherited properties, the same cellular reactions to stimuli of a higher order and the same cell complexes would be built up. But this is not the case; on the contrary, we observe a great variety of reactions to the same stimuli at different times in different cells. There can be several reasons. Due to environmental factors which interfere with cell groups before their activity is completed, there occur heterogeneous cell mutations which provide the different cell particles with varying protoplasmatic qualities. This heterogeneity may not be far reaching, and their abnormal activities may not even be demonstrable with our present chemical methods. However, varied dispositional reactiveness to endogenous and exogenous stimuli is laid down. There are also no characteristics in the cell structure from which the future physicochemical reactions to stimuli could be foreseen; yet it is *the kind of grouping of the most important chemical compounds of a cell which constitutes the basis for future, often aberrant, reactions of the organism*. Therefore, such cells will be prone to react prematurely or excessively to endogenous or exogenous stimuli. Due to its physicochemical properties, each and every cell of an organism possesses a different threshold and a different reactiveness to stimuli. These congenital qualities endow the cell complex to discharge endogenous and exogenous stimuli instinctually, as it were. Subsequently these instinctual discharge mechanisms lead, by way of repetition, to what constitutes the functional "memory" of a cell or of an organ system (Driesch).

This explains why the organism becomes accustomed—or better, is compelled—to respond to the same stimulus always in the same manner. This process paved the way for the development of the instinctual mechanisms. Thus, the individual instinctual responses are reaction formations due to chemical processes which continuously repeat themselves in the same manner and constitute the patterned and purposeful function of a cell complex. The transformations of one energy into another—especially into movement—are based on endogenous chemical processes in the cell, and are the basic schema of all responses to stimulation. From this point of view, the quality of the stimulus is of minor importance, since all stimuli lead to, or develop from, chemical processes which are finally discharged in movement. Whether we deal with simple reflectory or with instinctually evoked movements, or with complicated actions, they differ only by their complexity from the unicellular process.

If a cell is inhibited in its "instinctual" response to a stimulus from without or from within, the subsequent chemical process will tend to be discharged in a different form than movement, if that is possible. Otherwise the accumulation of the waste products will lead to the cell's death. Before this state is reached, however, a condition develops which a person subjectively perceives as unrest, unpleasure, anxiety. *Here we encounter* the *first signs of a conversion*. However, so far we are still mystified as to what cell processes correspond to these factors, and whether there are any which lead to the transformation of a specific physiologic process into a specific psychic one.

Whatever the case may be, the concept of a psychophysical parallelism must be rejected, for nothing parallel occurs here. The temporal coincidence of psychic and physical manifestations develops from the *identity* of these processes.

The forces which continually stimulate the catalytic process in the organism are the hormones. It is clear that these endocrine factors influence the chemical process in the organism, thereby altering cell activity. Likewise, the psychological process acts upon the hormonal activity of the endocrine glands which govern the metabolic processes leading to hypo- or hyperactivity of the cellular process. The hormonal secretion aims at a stimulation of cell activity to transmit the cell products into the blood stream and thereby to perpetuate the anabolic and catabolic processes. The energy set free by the elimination of these biochemical substrates equals the amount of tension released.

It has been shown that before this intermediary process in the cell compound reaches its completion, a condition exists which manifests itself as unpleasure. Its degree depends on the driving energy produced in this process. This energy has to pass freely through the organism in order to safeguard the psychophysiologic homeostasis. The transitory feeling of tension concurs with the transmission of the hormonal products of the germ cells into all cell units, a condition which finally calls for the discharge of the generated energy. The emotional release is an intricate psychic process (Urbantschitsch).

How can homeostasis of the chemical-humoral processes within the cell systems be assured? First of all, the biochemical adaptations have to be activated to keep the sensory threshold as low as possible whenever and as long as a discharge of the endogenous energizing substances has to be delayed. This may manifest itself in a lowered reaction to or avoidance of external stimuli. However, even these protective devices may not suffice. This will then result in a premature, or insufficient, deranged discharge of the unpleasure-producing substance which throws the physiologic process out of balance. The organism will be able to master this disturbed equilibrium by calling upon synergetically and compensatorily acting cell structures. In the absence of such a possibility for restoring the equilibrium, the cell system begins to show signs of dysfunction. The result is what we call sickness. It is perceived as unpleasure.

Waste products which are not eliminated lead to a compensatory cell activity to offset the unpleasure. However, the cell's memory retains the unpleasurable experience it once had, even after compensatory processes have restored the equilibrium in the whole cell economy. From then on the altered function becomes stabilized. The lower the threshold for the stimulus falls, the more probable it is that the disturbance will be permanent, although the original cause for the change in the metabolic cell process may no longer exist. Each time the memory of this unpleasure is evoked, it will be transformed into a changed activity of the cell systems. This transformation appears as one of the *primary forms of a leap from the psychic into the organic*. In fact, it was originally only the effect of the previously organic upon the organic and can be compared with the oligodynamic chemical process.

If a copper wire is kept in a bottle with water for a certain period, the bottle will retain its disinfectant faculty, although in a declining measure, and will impart it to any ensuing content a long time after the wire has been removed. This is due to that peculiarity which is known as the *oligodynamic* effect at a distance. Likewise, the waste products of the cells may then exert a stimulating effect even after elimination, similar to the oligodynamic effect. Even when no structural changes can be proved, the aftereffects may still be present. But since new exogenous stimulation recurs continually, the protoplasmatic cell processes will not be transformed into motion quantitatively. Therefore a bodily condition will result which is reflected as a feeling of unpleasure. An adaptation can finally be achieved only by zymoplastic changes.

The specific kind of stimuli acting upon the cell complex is not of crucial importance. Any difference in their effect will depend on whether it falls on a more or less prepared ground. Thus the pre-existent organic condition is decisive.

If biochemical processes in a cell system can lead to psychic conditions which in their simplest form manifest themselves as pleasure or unpleasure, then it is understandable that a cellular activity can be restored to normal only through a change of the psychophysiologic conditions. The pathways which the organism chooses to attain that stage will vary, depending on the resistances it has to overcome. *Whenever it chooses the wrong way in its defense, it will persist by repetition until a more suitable adjustment is possible.*

The memory of a cell system or of a whole organism to react in a deviated form to certain stimuli, whether it is based on inheritance or derived from a previous traumatic experience, may lead to a state of emotional tension which, combined with a heightened threshold to certain stimuli, presses for an uncompromising solution. This can be effected best by discharging the emotional tension, i.e., the pent-up libido, into other channels which in turn may lead to functional disorders in cell systems and organs of other parts of the body. Once an individual has chosen this means of defense against certain stimuli, and has maintained it by repetition, he will forever renounce the adequate discharge, in other words, the abreaction of emotions via the proper channels. Moreover, the continual repetition will produce functional disturbances in unrelated parts, thus assuring some kind of relief. The development of the organic disorders in hysteria might occur in this manner. The disorder is continuously kept alive by the residues of incompletely discharged affects, because disposition and coercion from within have finally rendered the organism incapable of releasing them in an adequate manner.

I have here come again to the starting point of my discussion in which I attempted to trace the psychophysiologic processes from their earliest sources to the conversion symptom. There is always a danger of losing the safe ground of facts, and to drift into the realm of speculation. As far as possible I have adhered to facts, for only they can lead us to new facts.

Part III

FELIX DEUTSCH:

The presentation of these two papers led to further discussions which were carried on in monthly meetings of the workshop for three years. They finally led to common agreement that Freud's concept of the conversion should be broadened and recognized as a continuous process lasting throughout life from the earliest phases of psychic development to maturity. This assumption served as a common denominator for the clinical papers which follow.

Part III

6.

SYMBOLIZATION AS A FORMATIVE STAGE OF THE CONVERSION PROCESS

FELIX DEUTSCH, M.D.

When reopening a discussion of the role which symbolization plays in the conversion process, it is imperative to recall Freud's statements regarding the basic concept of psychoanalysis.

"The psychoanalytic theory," Freud (1939) once said, "does not by any means fail to point out that neuroses have an organic basis—though it is true that it does not look for that basis in any pathologic-anatomical changes and provisionally substitutes the conception of organic functions for the chemical changes which we should expect to find, but which we are at present unable to apprehend."

This concise statement builds a bridge to an apprehension of the origin of the conversion process. The body represents to an individual the very reality which he cannot deny because to do so he would have to deny his existence. A newborn child knows only one reality, i.e., his body which he can feel, touch, and perceive with his senses. Nothing exists beyond this reality. The child soon discovers that what he once felt as part of himself is temporarily or permanently lost. This first awareness of a loss is the origin of a fantasy

75

or illusion, because what is no longer in the realm of, or attached to, the body has disappeared and now belongs to another reality, so to speak. The child reacts to this loss of an object with the attempt to regain it, to retrieve this part of himself, by imagining it (Deutsch, 1940). Attempts of this nature continue throughout life and can be considered as the origin of the conversion process.

From this point of view, it may be justifiable to broaden the concept of conversion, and above all to see in it a continually active process. I expressed this opinion many years ago (1924) (see Chapter 5). It was based on clinical observations which were in accordance with Freud's concept that the sense of reality originates from the projection of sensory perceptions of one's own body onto objects outside of it, since external objects are perceived as if severed from the body and lost. This separation leads to the continual wish to restore the loss of the bodily wholeness. The objects outside become reunited with the body by way of symbolization. I propose to call this process "retrojection." The physiologic functions of those body parts which have become the representatives of these symbolized objects are for this reason modified on account of the process of symbolization.

The character of these functions depends on the role the symbolized objects play in the unconscious. However, they will remain subject to Freud's constancy principle. Every change in the equilibrium of the physiologic function is conditioned in part by the conversion process which is forever functionally interrelated with the specific bodily part through the memory symbol. Whenever the latter returns, it enters into the physiologic process. The memory symbol has thus developed from a specific sensory perception of one's own body, which has been projected onto the external object. This specific sensory stimulus then serves as the mediator for the retrojection of the lost object onto that organ system which is its symbolic representation.

The memory symbols deposited in the body determine the character of the conversion process and also when and why it leads to a symptom formation. From this point of view the source of the symptom is the wish for, and the flight from, a symbolized object which stirs up an emotional process aimed at undoing the loss. This process awakens a memory in the form of a sensory percept which serves as a warning signal against a tabooed wish. The object of this wish was originally connected with this very sense perception, the memory of which has been repressed. Instead of it, a substitute object may be remembered which is linked to another kind of sensory perception, but one which is allowed to become conscious. However, if no surrogate object is available, conversion symptoms are formed. This can lead to partial or complete inhibition or to hyperactivity of a bodily function. In either event, the conversion symptom serves as a protective mechanism, the action of which is equivalent to the amount of anxiety to be prevented.

If this prevention through a conversion symptom does not suffice, anxiety breaks through, and the ego has to call upon other defense mechanisms to safeguard its integrity. The organic symptom is the protective device against an impending loss of the object which has been retrieved through retrojection and which rests symbolized in the body, where it maintains the body's unity.

Freud (1916-1917) described symbolism as an ancient but obsolete mode of expression. He recommended using the word "symbol" in a specific and restricted sense, because "all kinds of indications warn us against lumping it together with other forms of indirect representations without being able to form any clear, conceptual picture of their distinguishing features. . . . We must admit," he remarks further, "that we cannot at present assign quite definite limits to our conception of a symbol, for it tends to merge into substitution, etc., and even approaches closely to illusion."

From this point of view I consider symbolization as one of the most important factors which are immanent in the conversion process and which alter the physiologic processes from the beginning of life. It fuses together the body parts which as symbolic representations have become separated and can only become reunited by being given symbolic meanings. The unconscious becomes infiltrated by the symbolizations which build a bridge to the conscious by acting as amorphous afterimages. They may fade into the unconscious, but when re-evoked they become the precursors of the conversion symptom.

This tendency toward symbolization stems, according to Jones (1916), from the need of repression, because "only what is repressed is symbolized, and only what is repressed needs to be symbolized." This postulate precludes the assumption that the capacity for symbolization can be inborn (Hartmann, 1955). Nevertheless, the idea has recently been advanced that the infant is born with a symbolic capacity which contradicts the common conception that symbolism constitutes the expression of the fantasy world and its material denotes external objects (Rodrigué, 1956). This supports the assumption that "symbols may arise in a last resort from bodily perceptions which are common to all mankind" (Rycroft, 1956). According to this point of view, the symbolic activity is determined phylogenetically, as are the various instinctual impulses. However that may be, the conceptualization of the interdependence of perception and symbolization has recently taken deeper roots in psychoanalytic theory.

I have tried to approach this postulate from a clinical standpoint and have indicated the close relationship of the intersensory perception with the primary and secondary processes. Jones (1911) always adhered to the opinion that each individual re-creates his symbolism anew by perception, and Kubie (1953) likewise held unequivocally that "the autogeny of all symbolic processes has some of its roots in our evolving percepts and concepts of the body."

Whether the beginning of symbolization presupposes a complete ego function is a question the answer to which depends on when this onset is assumed to take place. Since in my opinion this happens at the earliest period of life, one can only think of a rudimentary ego functioning at that time. It is unlikely that this ego makes use of sexualized energy. Therefore symbolization precedes identification. Hence symbol formation begins together with the primary processes and starts before a relationship to constant objects is formed.

Much attention has been directed recently to the feeling of object loss as a ferment for the symbolization process (Lorand and Feldman, 1955). I wish to emphasize that each part of the body possesses the potentiality for the symbolic expression of loss and separation. This loss evokes anxiety which, as Freud stated, is a separation anxiety. Hence it calls for replacement. A more highly developed ego turns to different parts of the body which are adequately symbolized and may serve as substitutes for the loss. I have always insisted that there is an interchangeability of organs as far as their symbolic value is concerned. My emphasis on this is due to the fact that an imbalance in the feeling of loss of symbolized organ systems will determine the kind of conversion process set into action. The symbolization of the body is formative and functionally overdetermined.

Freud has clarified the meaning of the interchangeability of organs in his paper, "On the Transformation of Instincts, with Special Reference to Anal Erotism" (1916b). He refers to the fact that in the unconscious the conceptions "faeces, child and penis are seldom distinguished and are easily interchangeable," emphasizing that in the symbolic language of dreams, as well as in everyday speech, both child and penis are replaced by a single symbol common to both, i.e., the word "little." This proves that an organic correspondence reappears in the mind as an unconscious identity. In the example which Freud gives, the form and size of an organ are used as connecting symbolic links. Since then we have learned that there exist many sensory perceptual links which can serve as the symbolic tie and for which the form plays only a minor role. When they serve as symbols they will determine the threshold of their perceptivity. This threshold can be lowered to zero, a condition which I may call "sensory amnesia." Seen from this angle, the unconscious is the sum total of lost sensory perceptions lowered beyond the threshold for certain sensory elements.

Freud (1916b) once raised the question "whether substitution of the male genital through another limb, the foot or hand, may be called symbolic." He believed that his terminology was justified. These symbols, he held, are sexual symbols. However, the libidinization is coordinated with the process of symbolization. Only when the fantasy and dream world is embedded in the reality of the body, does the process of symbolization begin. Previous to that, however, the body or body parts of the lost object are searched for in one's own body. The sense perceptions evoked by this search are very likely forerunners of dream symbolism. Freud said that knowledge of dream symbolism is unconscious in the dreamer's mind. The same is true for the organ symbolism which is unconscious in the waking state. The body ego owes its development to a great extent to the incorporation of another one into itself. The process of symbolization is, in this respect, similar to that of identification. However, symbolization originates in the need to make good for the loss of the body's integrity by reintegrating into it adequate substitutes.

The symbolization substitutes the amount of loss which the lost object represented to the individual. If a loss occurs in relation to different objects at the same time, the need for symbolization becomes greater than a normal physiological function can warrant. From this point of view, it seems that the origin of a conversion symptom is due to an imagined loss of different *part objects*. The degree of cathexis depends on the intensity of the libidinal relationship to the lost object as well as on the number of other objects symbolized in an organ system. Furthermore, the loss of an object mobilizes the need for its restoration in different organ systems which once participated in the symbolization process.

If we take for granted that all instinctual drives have a biological origin, we must also conclude that whenever they emerge from their repression, they will have simultaneous expression because of their *identical* origin. The specific sensory stimulus can either come from without, or can be an illusion. No matter which is the case, the given psychodynamic situation determines the sensitivity to the stimulus, or rather, its actual threshold. The different sensory stimuli are signposts as well as warning signals for the ego. They become intensified, multiplied, and unified, when the ego feels the approaching danger. This is proof of the complexity of the repressive process. It is also a reflection of the defensive efforts which the ego makes to protect itself against anxiety.

These defensive efforts can be fully understood only if the interaction of the sensory perceptions and their related psychic elements can be traced back to their earliest sources and shown as an entity. In the course of analysis there appears a certain vacillation of sensory and intersensory perceptivity, because when a psychic stimulus presses for discharge, the physiological process initiated by the stimulus that led to a sensory reaction continues the psychological process in another form and has to be repressed or must be fully discharged. For this reason, a continual realignment of the synesthetic system takes place.

On several occasions I have pointed out (1939, 1946, 1948) that the establishment of an ego-governed instinctual-sensory pattern depends largely on how far the ego is able to use certain sensory perceptions for its defense. The more these sensory functions have been drawn into the protective mechanism during the development of the ego, the more indissolubly will this pattern be cemented into the personality structure. The ego keeps these regressive pathways wide open in case of a need for retreat, and uses the devices of repetition compulsion derived from biological functions as guides to safeguard its integrity.

CASE HISTORY

The foregoing discussion may be illustrated by a series of analytic sessions with a patient, a physiologist, whose analysis had been concerned for a long time with the painstaking working through of his identification with his mother (and sister) and his feminine attitude toward his father. The patient's feminine fantasies were expressed mainly in the respiratory and intestinal tract; it was possible to trace them back in their concealed form to his earliest childhood. The ego's attempt to master them had led to the development of a compulsive-neurotic personality which could adjust itself to reality only through expiatory, compulsive activities. The latter were sublimated in the patient's professional work, experimental research in circulatory and pulmonary diseases, and represented a continuation of his infantile curiosity concerning procreative processes. This curiosity also led him to search for a growth in his own body, and to his denial of a difference in the sexes. The analysis dealt with these fantasies for some time.

The associative material of this first period of analysis yielded memories of the patient's childhood, when he was playing with his sister three years his junior. (This sister was pregnant at this time of the analysis.) He had no memories at all about his mother's pregnancy with this sister. Ideas with regard to the dangers of childbirth led to remarks concerning Caesarean section, cardiac and pulmonary operations, as well as operations for kidney stones and gall stones. His mother had a kidney operation and suffered with gall stones. With the word "stones" he associated "dead child," remembering a passage from the poem "The Alder King," in which a *father* is carrying his *dead* child in his arms. This led first to memories of his infantile curiosity about the origin of that child. He then remembered that each time he visited his father's grave when he was a boy of thirteen, he placed a little stone on it. The father had died following an intestinal sickness when the patient was twelve. These small stones, he explained, had the *symbolic* purpose of preventing the dead from rising again, by forming a new grave stone.

The word "stone" had other associative links. *Kinesthetic* sensations led to a posture with the hand under the head, because his *head* felt as heavy as a *stone*. He then thought of "Lot's wife" who was transformed into a pillar of salt, like a stone. Obviously here were blended ideas of both birth and death, whereby the father, mother and child are threatened with death. Their loss has to be redeemed. During the following analytic hours such ideas became condensed and expressed indirectly in "Stone of the Sages," "I am in his good books" (*"Stein im Brett"*), "A stone lies in my stomach." These phrases were followed by audible stomach and intestinal *noises*. They were specific rudimentary conversion symptoms. Immediately thereafter the patient had the impression of double *vision,* an illusion which he had reported previously from time to time. This was the visual expression of his multiple personality and appeared mostly when he became drowsy and talked in a kind of reverie.

This condition was like an attempted flight from reality permitting him to split his image into a male and female part but which still were fused together. Whenever a confrontation with this conflict became too threatening to his ego, he used this sensory perception as a defense which permitted him to see double both himself and one of the external objects. As a child he had once found out that he could squint, and he had practiced it since he noted that he thereby could see double.

The preverbal forerunners of the memory of anal birth fantasies and their tabooed gratifications were now manifested in *painful* sensations in the back. They radiated into his left leg when he was lying on the couch. Again he thought of the "Alder King" and the *father* riding on a horse, with the dead child in his arms. This association led to *auditory* sensations. He began to listen to the *noises* of the radiator in the room which made him anxious. After a long silence he associated "toilet noises," adding a memory of watching his mother urinating or defecating on the toilet. This brought to his mind the cries of women in labor. He became drowsy, and the picture on the opposite wall turned into a burning mountain on a hilly road. He recalled his native town, and that the street in which he lived was called Hills Road. With "mountain" he associated "breast" and *mons veneris* and the phrase from the fairy tale Snow White: "Mirror, mirror on the wall—who is the most beautiful of all?"

In the following weeks the analytic hours dealt chiefly with further working through of the patient's birth fantasies and his masculine protest against them. These were intermingled with visual, hypnagogic impressions in which the picture on the opposite wall changed to a volcano and then to a Japanese Geisha. It was the image of his own femininity which he began to reject. He found himself acting out this conflict by professional proficiency, behaving aggressively in competition with his coworkers, particularly those in whom he noticed his own anal, feminine character traits. When a manuscript which he had submitted for publication was returned with the request to shorten it, he refused to do it— as if it had meant the *irretrievable loss of a part* of himself.

It seemed like having to give up the whole, like being doomed.

During this period the patient had spells of right-sided headaches which were similar to, and yet different from, the migraine attacks he had had since his tenth year. They usually appeared when he felt hungry, and *disappeared*—as they did now—when he had something to eat. Before his tabooed and repressed wishes could be verbalized, they appeared in preverbal manifestations—auditory, visual, and through pain. They were due to the symbolizations pertaining to the images of specific objects. The ego used these sensory perceptions by tuning up their threshold according to the need for its defense against the emergence of the repressed wishes, but also for their gratification in a symbolized form.

This conversion process led again to sensory manifestations in connection with his passive, anal fantasies. During this process he often remained silent for a long time. He had a feeling as if his mind went blank—as if even the sound of his own voice were too much for him. He listened to the noise of the cars on the street, and would have liked to run away, as he said. The noise of the radiator irritated him and he wondered why he had never noticed it before. He found the air in the room *stuffy,* and thought of an old man who had claimed that his landlord was trying to kill him through poisonous gas. Reminded of it, the patient began to yawn and felt as if choked.

He became drowsy and again began to see double. At the same time he covered his ears with his arms and remained silent for the rest of the session. In the following hours these intersensory perceptions and the related behavior gave way to verbalized associative material essentially concerning the self-assertion of his masculinity and activity.

To sum it up briefly: auditory, olfactory, and visual sensory perceptions, together with motor behavior, had preceded and then accompanied the verbal expression of the patient's masculine strivings. His hypersensitivity to any kind of auditory stimuli served as a defense against his passive anal wishes toward the symbolized objects. The sensation of headache and pain in the right eye signalized the danger ahead. Here is certainly also expressed the superego threat. We can assume that the superego is not only built up from the *"Hörhaube,"* but by all sensory signals. However, one may become the specific "siren" which warns the ego. There are indications that the more sensory perceptions are involved in the superego structure, the more threatening it may become. This complex danger signal seemed to stem from the repressed memory symbols or images laid down by retrojection into the related sensory organs. These sensory perceptions were always intimately related to specific objects, and their appearance as preverbal associations at a certain stage of analysis could be considered as a part of the analytic process which released the repressed unconscious wishes.

The patient's abandonment of his feminine identifications was followed by increasing castration anxiety when he began to assert his masculine role. In reality he acted it out in aggressive and competitive behavior toward his equals, and revolt against his superiors. Gradually the associative anal material diminished. The awareness of this change in him he summed up in the sentence: "The girl within me has to die in order that I may become a man." He realized that he would have to abandon his unconscious pregnancy fantasies together with the fear that the pregnancy would end in stillbirth. This threat led him to think of his own death and even of suicide. These thoughts were accompanied by fluctuations in his sensitivity to intrinsic and extrinsic visual, auditory, and pain stimuli, depending on his more active or passive leanings. On the one hand, he became very interested in collecting money from different foundations for research. He ridiculed those who regarded money as filthy and contaminated, and in particular criticized a colleague in whom he recognized those anal character traits which he had seen in himself. He decided not to waste any more time with doubts as to his efficiency. In fact, he found that he was already able to function better professionally.

He felt free to act, but he did not trust his good fortune because—as he worded it—he was afraid of the Erinyes, the spirits of revenge. He described "luck" as the ability to overcome inhibitions which had doomed his activities to failure. He called the Erinyes the "dampers of presumption," whom Zeus had designated to punish the presumptuous. Therefore he felt ill at ease in his new role as a leader. Feelings of guilt and fear of punishment disturbed him. He considered himself a thief when he began to keep company with a girl whom he intended to marry. He encountered her father's disapproval, and he ventured the idea of discontinuing analysis. During this period of acting out there were no manifestations of visual, auditory, or olfactory perceptions. Instead, there appeared kinesthetic sensations in the left arm and leg (numbness). These brought to his mind a man with a thrombosis after an intravenous injection which resulted in the loss of his left arm. He associated memories of genital play with his sister, being puzzled not to see a penis, and thinking she must have lost it. During this session he complained of increasing headache on the left side, which lasted only a very short time, but changed to a feeling as if his head were swelling up like a balloon. He thought of a bullfrog that blows itself up until it busts, and he had a sensation as if his whole body were floating.

In a kind of reverie he saw the figure "8," a pair of spectacles, a brassière, and he thought of breasts. He claimed that his mother had nursed him for ten months, which was longer than she had nursed his sister. He began to shiver, recalling that he had often hid cushions under his jacket, imagining he had breasts. With a deep sigh he crossed his arms over his chest.

Discussion

These observations during a certain period of analysis may suffice to demonstrate the continual process of conversion. They also show how the patient used sensory perceptions to become reunited with the lost objects by symbolization.

The conversion symptom is made up of some pieces that interact according to a few distinct rules. The variety of symptoms arises from the many different ways in which the basic pieces are put together. One has only to know how the pieces are put together to understand the differences in the different specific symptoms. In order to understand the complexity it is necessary to break up the cathected symbolized objects into the fundamental particles. We ultimately have to find the smallest pieces and look up the rules governing them on different levels. Then it can be shown that certain types of phenomena can be called fundamental. These types develop on account of certain energies in action which determine their structure. Although the nucleus of the different types is in many instances the same, the psychic energy arranges the particles around the nucleus.

Conversion symptoms can therefore be explained in terms of particles of certain sensory perceptions. The puzzle is how the psychic energies can alter the physiologic equilibrium. That riddle can be solved only when we go down to smaller pieces of psychic phenomena, in order to interpret the total phenomenon of the conversion symptom. It seems that they can be fully understood only in terms of their interaction with other particles of individual entities. Then we may find a coherence of these particles, and also the main rules governing the interaction of the pieces.

Freud (1900) mentions in connection with the origin of perception, that we become aware of the living objects around us by perception complexes which come forth from them, but which are fused with memories of similar perceptions of our own body. The memories of these sensations are associatively interlinked with reactive movements once experienced in oneself. Hence the objects are recognized perceptively through recollective mechanisms which are rooted in sensory perceptions of one's own body.

I assume that these recollective sensations originate from stimulation of any kind of sense perceptions when their threshold becomes lowered. The reactive movement is the response to the sensory signal of an instinctual feeling, and represents a turning to, or away from, the object (Deutsch, 1954). Thus these feelings are derived from a sensory perception which serves as a warning signal against a wish toward a symbolized object. The desired object is always closely connected with a series of sensory perceptions. The wish has become repressed but is continually reawakened by sensory stimuli. Originally, sensory perception was directed toward the own body only, and there *sensu strictiori* was without an object. When primary sensory perceptions become libidinized, they gradually spread over the objects, keeping them and their perceiver in continuous contact with past and present reality. At the same time, they become the mediators for the symbolized objects.

My concept of symbolized objects is that they are a composite of very early cathected sense perceptions which were once formed into a body ego. These sensory constellations have become fused through partial identification with sensorily perceived parts of other objects. The earliest perceived objects with whom the most intensive, long-lasting sensorial contact occurred, contain the meaning of these objects, the loss of which equals a body loss.

In different phases of development these constellations are hierarchically built up and differently grouped. Thus the instinctual stimulation of one sense perception corresponds always to a certain image. But there is, as has been pointed out by Schilder (1935), "no isolated sense impression; *synesthesia* is one of the basic principles of perception." Therefore, the specificity is determined structurally, and by the time level. Here I may again point out that one cannot deal with the conception of symbolization without taking the phenomena of synesthesia into consideration. The first and for a long time the only scientific recognition of synesthesia appeared in 1912 when G. T. L. Sachs described his studies on dual perceptions.

Ferenczi (1916-1917) mentioned these phenomena when he tried to explain pollution dreams without orgasm as "reactions to stimulations of heterogeneous sensory areas."

As early as 1912, Hug-Hellmuth and Pfister introduced this concept independently of each other. Hug-Hellmuth referred to the fusion of sounds and noises with visual sensations, particularly of color, i.e., visual impressions may create auditory sensations. In this connection she mentions cases of optic and acoustic synesthesia which were sometimes connected with smell, taste, and touch sensations, and which she called "secondary sensory imaginations," or "photisms." She found that these fusions of sensory perceptions were widespread among children, but could not give a satisfactory explanation. Obviously one is dealing here with very short-lasting perceptions which never became sufficiently conscious and very likely belong to the primary processes.

Steinbrügge (1912) suggested that many individuals who associate words or perceptions with colors may have had these dual sensations in their earliest childhood. The combinations of sensory impressions must have become engrained in their unconscious and will reappear associatively only when the repressed memory becomes conscious.

Susan Isaacs (1948) has pointed out that "the earliest fantasies bound up with sensory experience are characterized by those qualities which Freud described as belonging to the primary process." These fantasies are reactions to the loss of the body unity due to the projections of bodily sensations to external objects, a loss which has to be renounced. This leads to the symbolization of these objects in the attempt of redeeming them. This formulation is in accordance with Isaacs' concept that symbolization becomes the forerunner of the identification process, which goes back to the child's endeavor to rediscover in every object his own organs and their functioning. Their retrojection and symbolization are, as I believe, the elements of the conversion process. It is very unlikely that the first sensation of loss can be traced back to one traumatic experience. Therefore it is debatable whether symbolization has its origin in the loss of the mother's breast, as is commonly assumed, or whether its source lies rather in bodily sensations not related merely to those of mouth and breast contact, although Freud (1939) stated, "The phylogenetic function has so much the upper hand over accidental experience that it makes no difference whether a child has really sucked on the breast or been brought up on the bottle and never enjoyed the tenderness of a mother's care. The development takes the same path in both cases; it may be that in the latter event his later longing is all the greater." I am inclined to include among the earliest experiences of loss also sensations which originate in different experiences than the mouth-breast contact.

The breaking through of repressed memories seems to lead over a threshold lowered for specific sensory perceptions into the preconscious, where they are arrested by the appearance of heightened stimuli from other sensory perceptions. All these sensory stimuli are the precursors of symbols of— as we know today—synesthetically cathected objects with which they are connected. These recollections remain repressed as long as the sensory stimuli belonging to the object can be kept below the threshold.

If the primary sensory perceptions of light, sound, touch, etc., remained uncathected, they would follow exclusively the physiological laws. However, in the course of psychic development, these perceptions become symbolized and evoke the whole past history of a specific object relationship. Thus the symbolizations of sensory perceptions serve as a feedback for physiological processes.

By and large, my concept of objects stems from the ego's faculty of manipulating sense perceptions in the earliest cognition of objects, and of forming a sensory configuration which becomes specific for certain objects, as for instance the parental figures. In the analytic process the representations of the patient's object world become destructuralized and derealized, with a goal of synthesizing them again into a new form which the ego can accept (Deutsch, 1954).

The supply of pregenital demands in this new form can, through the treatment, be brought into agreement with the genital demands and with reality. When these demands become too great, and when the ego has already used up too many organ systems in its defense, it usually tries to re-establish its equilibrium by calling upon these sensory organs which sustain the homeostasis on a lower level of development and which have served for the gratification of polar demands. As I have pointed out, the ego deals with this offer by rendering the sense perceptions involved hyper- or hyposensitive and hyper- or hypofunctioning, respectively, depending on their symbolized potentialities.

Recently it was suggested that the "mystery" of the leap from the mind to the soma will be resolved from the physiologic angle by the *existence of potential fields in the brain* (Strauss, 1955). According to this concept, "the unconscious becomes invaded by the symbolizations which build the bridge to the consciousness. They create the particular setting of potential fields which through continuous repetition become structuralized and lead to that which is called conscious and unconscious experience." (These statements remind one of Hering's *Seele,* and his contention that the organism never forgets any previous physical happening.) Consciousness fades out when its coherence sustained by the electrical potentials in the brain becomes altered by the intrusion of *symbolic* forces which call for a *regrouping of sensory constituents*. This process stems from primitive, abstract, objectless (or better, autoplastic), primary processes which lead to different chemical and neurogenic constellations resulting finally in electric activities, the origin of mental processes. Originally, these primary processes were perceived only as noises and sounds expressing pleasure or unpleasure and pain, respectively.

This theory of Strauss, that mental processes are structural physical fields (a theory derived from Adrian's electrical brain field concept and from Koehler's Gestalt psychology) which he calls "the field identity theory," does not resolve the assumed contradiction between interaction of bodily and mental processes, but brings into focus one of the most important factors for the understanding of the "mysterious leap." It leads to potential constituents and then to a structuralized physical as well as to a mental unity, which, however, is not permanent, but is influenced by the dynamics of psychic processes.

Impulses of any quality, chemical or neurogenic, lead to electrical stimulation and produce sensations which are mental constituents *par excellence*. They were originally and of necessity unconscious and may have been only sensations governed simply by the existing physical processes. In the beginning they must have been perceived in the body as being parts of one's own body. When these impulses cease, the process which leads to the sensory sensation will gradually become completed.

The specificity of the awareness of an object or the specificity of using a certain organ system to express the unconscious mental process consists in the specific synesthetic unity of sensory organs at the lowest abstract, i.e., objectless level.

The first object awareness can only be that of one's own body, which may be called the "self." Gestalt psychology speaks of the concrete unity of perception, a unity that evolved on different levels of experience. Of chief importance is how the grouping developed on the most primitive level. The unity based on the grouping can be split if the disturbing stimuli are sufficiently strong. Therefore it is not only a dynamic self-organizing process in the nervous system which accounts for the facts of the organization or grouping in perception. The dynamic process is governed by the dynamisms within the psychic apparatus: id-ego-superego. They produce the oscillations in the potential fields of the brain pervading the tissue as a continuum (Gerard, 1936).

What is perceived via the sensory stimulus is only a sensation which is specific for the special sense organ, whether it is the retina or the auditory apparatus or the olfactory organ or the tactile end organs, etc. This sensation becomes more complicated but is qualitatively not different as far as the visceral organs are concerned. Here enters the sensation of pain: all inside sensations are referred sensations, as if coming from other sense organs, which serve as signals either to prevent pain or to announce pleasure (Fuller, Easler, and Smith, 1950).

We may assume that any kind of sensorimotor perceptivity depends on the harmony of the id, ego, and superego forces. However, what creates the threshold for this perceptivity is determined by the process of symbolization. This concept does not undervaluate the importance of complementary characteristics of environmental objects or of events which may exert their influence, provided they are extremely well timed and favorable for their retrojection, in accordance with the ego-id-superego balance. It seems to be decisive that the ego has had sufficient time to withstand the great demands of the id as well as the threat of the superego forces at all levels of development. However, the chief emphasis, in my opinion, lies in the way in which sensory functional processes necessary for the awareness of reality are projected onto and insolubly tied to objects, and how after the cathexis of these objects they are retrojected onto the body, where they remain *symbolized* and dormant, thereby influencing the vacillations of the physiological processes.

There exists always a free-floating sensory perceptivity which the ego seizes to retroject the lost objects and resynthesize them through symbolization with the body from where they originated. This necessitates a sort of specific organ tropism which is presupposed for the timely release of rudimentary conversion symptoms, whenever repressions are lifted. The intensity of this tropism depends on the degree of the confluence of different symbolized sensory and visceral perceptions. Their amalgamation is pre-eminent, as we know, in the genitals and in their displaced organ representation. This convergence of so many symbolized sensory qualities in those organs which serve the gratification of sexual drives makes their demands sometimes almost irresistible.

We may assume that the orgastic sensations experienced in the sexual act fulfill the illusion of resuscitation and of a reunification of the lost objects with one's own body in a symbolized form. In this sense the orgasm is a true conversion symptom. In pregenital conversion symptoms the confluence of the symbolized sensory perceptions is only regressively displaced.

In conclusion, I wish to reaffirm that in view of the fact that the symbolization of external objects leads to a retrojection of these lost objects via sensory pathways onto and into the body where they remain immanent and dormant, we have to realize that a conversion process is continually in action and any manifestation of this process expressed in an altered organic function is only the end result, called conversion symptom. There is one altered organic function beyond which all conversion ends, i.e., death. This raises the question of the relation between the death instinct and the conversion process.

Freud (1939) made it quite clear how he wanted the death instinct to be understood: "I have myself been obliged to assert the existence of an 'aggressive instinct' . . . I prefer to call it the 'destruction' or 'death instinct'. . . . Its opposition to the libidinal instincts finds an expression in the familiar polarity of love and hate."

There can thus be no doubt that one of the most important roots of the death instinct is to be found in the ambivalence conflict. This can be understood only on the basis that the wish for destruction contained therein is directed from the *objects whom one wishes dead* onto one's own self. If this assumption is correct, then we must also assume that the instinct of self-preservation expresses this part of the ambivalence conflict which belongs to the feelings entertained toward the love object.

The hostile feelings toward the hated object lead in a kind of feedback to the destructive instincts, which must have their physiologic counterpart as a conversion process. The wish to redeem the object by retrojection overcompensates for revengeful feelings and may lead to an alteration of physiologic functions. This conversion process may end in self-destruction. When it coincides with an involutionary process—as in the aging body—it may even provoke an earlier death, depending on the intensity of the death instinct and on the organs involved in the process.

It is suggestive that a diseased organism will succumb sooner when the death instinct has as its target vital organs in which the inherent symbolizations promote a conversion process. The death instinct which stems from the aggressive drives can thereby be gratified. The reunion with the symbolized objects, even if the price for it is the destruction, or death, of one's own body, may sometimes create the feeling of equanimity (Euthanasia), because the revengeful destruction of the symbolized object has been achieved.

The whole concept of symbolization is presented in the hope that it may help fill the as yet unbridged gap which Freud called "the mysterious leap from the mental to the physical."[1]

---

[1] After the completion of this chapter, the article "Notes on Symbol Formation" by Hanna Segal (1957) appeared. Segal summarizes her thesis in the statement: "The process of symbol formation is, I think, a continuous process of bringing together and integrating the internal with the external, the subject with the object, and the earlier experiences with the later ones." This conception is in some respects in conformity with mine. However, the basis on which the author's ideas rest does not fall into line with the conceptualization dealt with in this discussion.

7.

THE ROLE OF IDENTIFICATION
IN THE CONVERSION PROCESS

ALFRED O. LUDWIG, M.D.

The concept that the conversion process involves restitution for loss and that lost objects are reunited with the body
by means of symbolization and identification has been already outlined (see Chapter 6). In the course of this process
the functions of the involved organs may be modified as the
symptom in the conversion process is elaborated.

Identification is one among many aspects of the conversion
process, and its role will be illustrated by some clinical examples.

The first patient is a sixty-year-old woman who has been
followed for over twenty years. In five years of intensive
psychoanalytic psychotherapy severe depressions and anxiety
were much improved. She suffered also from episodic compulsive overeating and obesity, mild rheumatoid arthritis,
peptic ulcer, and more recently from moderate to severe
bronchial asthma.

Her life began with severe emotional deprivation at the
time of delivery when her mother sustained a hemiplegia
which left her severely incapacitated. The patient was cared
for by an aunt who died when the patient was eighteen
months old and she was then sent to live with her maternal
grandmother whom she recalled as strict in training and who

concentrated on controlling thumb sucking. At the age of seven she was returned home to her mother to begin school.

She described severe outbursts of anxiety. These often occurred while she was dining with her father. Her mother would become ill upstairs, and her father would rush up to help while she herself would sit terrified at the table and hold herself together by thinking obsessively of some phrase, such as: "The maid is putting on the wrong plate." She felt that this kept her from "falling to pieces." It is likely that these phenomena were related to identification with a mother who appeared to be disintegrating. Later she "focused," that is, maintained contact with reality, by means of somatic symptoms.

During adolescence she felt that her father pushed her into the masculine role by setting high intellectual standards and by requiring the accomplishment of difficult physical tasks. During college and in subsequent years as her mother became progressively more helpless she was often called home to care for her.

The patient always had difficulty in expressing emotion. Unable to feel any grief at the age of eleven when her grandmother died, she was "saved" by her father's expression of sorrow which released emotion for her.

The transference had the nature of a mother-child relationship and sometimes became symbiotic in character. Any threat of separation from the therapist she felt as catastrophic. During therapeutic hours she was often so intensely anxious that she was unable to sit down and either stood or walked around the room. Anxiety could be precipitated by separation, by any loss, by any change in the mood of the therapist or by even a superficial change in the consulting room.

The nature of some of her fantasies was demonstrated by her reactions in a sleeping car. She was unable to tolerate an upper berth and even in a lower berth would find herself overcome by anxiety. She experienced a feeling of floating with the fantasy that "the train breathed for a whole litter of passengers." She recaptured reality by opening the shade and seeing people or things outside. At sea she became anxious as well as seasick and felt that she lacked a base of reference. In this situation she could regain control by focusing on a cloud "to provide a base of reference," and re-establish a sense of her own identity, her separateness, and her contact with reality.

Often she woke up in the middle of the night with ulcer pain. If she could think of her doctor as friendly and supporting, pain disappeared spontaneously without medication. On the other hand, if she were angry she thought of the doctor as hostile and unfriendly and then: "I have to gobble him up. He becomes painful to me as my parents were when I was a child and I have pain." In the latter instance discomfort continued in spite of medication.

These two alternatives afford insight into the nature of the conversion process at the moment of its occurrence. Relief of pain seemed to depend on the attitude toward the object. A beneficial result followed if the object remained "good," while withdrawal of libido to the body and continuation of symptoms took place if the object became "bad."

Another aspect of her attitude sheds more light on the process. She said, "I am sensitive to the slightest breath of a suspicion of rejection."

In part, because of projected hostility, she was prone to suspect rejection from any person who manifested either an unexpressed emotion or anxiety. It was discovered that admission of the presence of a given emotion which might not necessarily concern her was immediately reassuring. On one occasion she had a recurrence of somatic symptoms and indicated that she was concerned about a friend's welfare but afraid to inquire lest she be rejected. When she was made aware that she had been right when she sensed but misinterpreted the reasons for his anxiety, she immediately felt much more comfortable.

Apparently her need to identify was increased by any threat, whether it arose from within, perhaps by the appearance of an organic illness, or from without when she sensed discomfort in another person which she then referred to herself. Both situations aroused fear of rejection and set in motion the conversion process in an attempt to make restitution for the threatened object loss. Under these circumstances libido is withdrawn from the object and invested in an organ.

The important point is that it may be possible to reverse this process, regain contact and to interrupt the conversion.

If anxiety cannot be alleviated, passive dependent impulses are activated, and diffuse aggression and oral incorporative impulses are released. However "good" the object may have been, it becomes confused with and changed into the image of the original hostile mother. Thereby it becomes "bad" and is dealt with by introjection. As libido has been withdrawn from the object and invested in an organ, the relation to the object is now expressed in terms of the function or dysfunction of the organ so invested.

Freud (1914b) commented that one cannot actively love another person when one has a toothache. By this he meant that it is difficult to invest libido in an object when one's own body is noisily attracting attention. The converse may be postulated by stating that if one is unable to love an object or is separated from it, especially if it is invested with ambivalent feeling, the body tends to resolve the conflict by means of conversion with the development of an organic symptom.

Two additional examples illustrate the rapidity with which manifestations of the conversion process may appear and disappear.

A young woman who suffered from rheumatoid arthritis

was in psychoanalytic psychotherapy during a period when her joint disease was quiescent. During the interviews she was always extremely anxious and had difficulty in talking. At times she was even more tense, inhibited, and practically mute. Several days after such a state she could finally verbalize that she had had an altercation with her mother. In one such episode her mother urged her to go to work, although the patient had not finished school. She felt this advice was a threat of separation from her mother. She described the immediate appearance of extreme anxiety even as she talked with her mother. Within twenty-four hours she developed an effusion in one knee joint which subsided completely in the course of forty-eight hours.

In another patient with mild rheumatoid arthritis, grossly psychotic symptoms were a feature. At one time she was given an interpretation which implied rejection by her mother. Immediately she began to hallucinate that her parents were in the room and wished to harm her. Within a few hours she developed pain and swelling of her finger joints.

It has been suggested that the conversion process may be reversible. The last two examples demonstrate that a conversion process which has emerged rather suddenly may subside spontaneously under favorable circumstances. In the patient in whom the process seemed to be interrupted by therapeutic intervention, contact was re-established by "giving" in terms of correct interpretation of the existing complicated doctor-patient relationship. This successful communication seemed to restore the lost piece of reality (i.e., mother) and to facilitate the reinvestment of libido outside the body.

Patients of the type who react habitually to stress with somatic disorders appear to experience frustration in terms of rejection and may react secondarily by withdrawing libido from their objects. At this moment they are overwhelmed by destructive impulses which they feel and express as "I am beginning to die." They attempt to make restitution by means of the conversion process and cathect their organs with these destructive impulses. They now invest the organ with the ambivalent feelings formerly fastened on the object and produce symptoms to which they then cling as tenaciously as they formerly clung to the original object. Aware of their self-preservative function many patients refer to such symptoms as "their friend." By focusing on themselves they are able to avoid total annihilation. In differentiating hysteria from psychosomatic disorders, Karl Menninger (1938, p. 410) stated that in the former, organ function is sacrificed to preserve the organ, whereas in the latter the organ is sacrificed in order to preserve life.

Further illustration of some of the complicated manifestations of identification is afforded by the second case.

A forty-six-year-old man sought psychiatric treatment because of episodes of excessive drinking. In the very first interview he confessed that he thought "bisexuality" was related to the drinking and that for him drinking was a substitute for more overt expressions of homosexuality. During the drinking bouts he often talked with other men about the subject.

He was somewhat effeminate, witty and whimsical. As a hobby he directed plays to raise funds for Catholic parishes. He usually managed to choose subjects which were subtly anticlerical, and was quite aware of his intention to irritate the parish priests.

In his description each episode of drinking began "when my left foot deviates into a barroom," without any previous awareness of such intent. After drinking for several hours in a bar, he would buy a supply of liquor and continue to drink at home over Saturday and Sunday. As a rule he was able to return to work on Monday.

His soft-spoken, passive father was overruled at home. During the depression in the 1930's he left work and began to drink to excess. His dominating Yankee mother ruled the family. The patient remembered particularly "her mellifluous voice which made my hair stand on end when she called me."

There were four siblings, a brother six years older, a brother six years younger, and two sisters. One sister became a nun. The other sister never married and later sustained a "nervous breakdown." The patient's wife was a dominating redhead. Her only pregnancy ended in miscarriage at eight months. He was angry with her because "he had to be a mother to her," and he resented intensely her infertility. He was extremely envious of both his brother-in-law who had three children and of his older brother who had one son.

He felt "eternally damned" because of a homosexual seduction by his older brother when the patient was eight years old. The brother was athletic and eventually became a vaudeville acrobat. He later became alcoholic but is now abstinent and works as a bartender.

The patient was born prematurely. He was weak and sickly in childhood and admitted to having been spoiled by his mother. She would never tolerate any expression of anger, and whenever he showed any, he was given hot milk and put to bed.

His older brother played an important role during therapy. On one occasion the patient picked up a muscular young man near his brother's bar, took him to a hotel and masturbated him. He described disturbing "homosexual images" of a large muscular man with an erect phallus. He envied his brother's physique. His brother, in turn, admired the patient's "gift of gab." While he expressed profound hatred for his brother, he felt both that he could not get rid of him and also that his brother "would not let him go."

He was vain about his voice and prided himself on his diction. He made and enjoyed listening to recordings of his voice and liked to hear his voice come back to him from his pupils. He realized that he used his voice to gain approval.

He regarded his dramatic coaching as a substitute for his childlessness.

In a dramatic session, he attempted to seduce the therapist in an exact repetition of his brother's seduction of him when he was eight years old, and he was furious when the doctor failed to respond.

Eleven days after this piece of acting out, he became hoarse. Nothing abnormal was found by his own physician, but one month later a laryngologist discovered a carcinoma involving the left vocal cord. After therapy had destroyed the tumor as well as his vocal function, he blamed the doctors for not having warned him of this possibility. He likened the loss of his voice to castration. He felt "his voice had been emasculated" and he was furious when his coworkers could not hear him. This was associated with his father who had never raised his voice, could not be heard, and had referred all decisions to his wife.

Our interest is focused on the hypercathexis of the larynx and the voice. Through the medium of his mother's "mellifluous voice" it symbolized identification with her. It was used in the service of intense competition with his brother whose physical prowess he could only match with his voice. After the change in his voice which followed therapy, it represented identification with his soft-spoken passive father.

Unless it is associated with conflict, identification does not ordinarily produce disturbing symptoms. In this patient the father with whom he identified was invested with strong ambivalent feelings. He was disillusioned by his father's inadequacy and by his inability to protect him from his dominating mother. He was equally ambivalent about his mother. He identified with her through his voice which then became the symbol of his ego-alien femininity.

With his voice he achieved narcissistic gratification, he re-experienced his passive dependence on his mother, but he also used it to attack the Church, synonymous for him with authoritarian women. His voice symbolized the weak masculinity of his father as well as the destructive masculinity of his mother. With his voice he sought to neutralize and to destroy his hated brother with whom he could not compete physically, as well as to compensate for passive homosexual wishes toward him. His vocal function symbolized his conflict with his femininity, his identification with his weak father and like his father his own subjugation to his castrating mother. He also identified strongly with her. By coaching dramatics in which she was interested, he enjoyed hearing the echo of his mother's voice coming back from his pupils. His conscious pleasure in these activities masked his unconscious wishes to submit to her. In fantasy he probably subjugated his pupils as he formerly had been subjugated by his mother and by the nuns. On the other hand, his vocal function represented identification with the aggressor, that is, with his brother. This was acted out when he attempted to seduce the therapist.

His laryngeal function was strongly erotized: its service in symbolizing his masculine-feminine conflict was clear. There was much evidence that his left side symbolized his passive femininity. One recalls his opening statement about his left foot precipitating the drinking as well as the fact that he was left-handed and intensely resented having his writing changed to the right hand by the nuns. During treatment, as he recovered the memory of his fury with his teachers, he noticed a marked change in his handwriting away from the rigid spencerian style which he had habitually used before.

The cancer which he pictured as a feminine shoe button ironically involved his left vocal cord. His bisexual conflict, his intense ambivalence, and his sadomasochistic wishes to dominate and surrender in terms of both male and female objects were cathected on his "feminine" left side, but especially on his laryngeal function.

After the destruction of his voice, any passivity, even lying down, threatened him to the point where he could not sleep in a bed. Frightening, passive homosexual fantasies were undoubtedly activated. When he could not be heard at work, he expressed violently in the transference the hatred formerly directed at his mother, at his nun teachers and at his older brother who had seduced him. With increasing understanding of these events he could use his damaged voice more normally, and when his fears of impotence were allayed after successful sexual relations with his wife, he could again sleep flat in his bed.

In view of the large quantities of energy and the intensity of the conflict cathected in the larynx, one might have predicted that this man's vocal cords would become the seat of disease. Quite possibly the interference with his drinking, which served as a powerful cathexis of his homosexuality, dangerously shifted the cathexis to his larynx and may have precipitated the outbreak of the malignancy localized there.

Why did the larynx become so important in these cathexes? Perhaps some acute disease in the nature of a laryngitis had occurred coincident with an emotional disturbance early in childhood. From the emphasis which he placed on the qualities of his father's and mother's voices, both speech and hearing must have had a powerful meaning in terms of his relationships with them.

Not only is a high degree of erotization prerequisite for an organ to become involved in the conversion process, but it seems likely that a high degree of erotization of the given organ in the parent may lead to a focus in the same organ of the child as one of the important media for identification with a parent.

The erotization and cathexis of an organ function in a parent seems to lead to special awareness of this particular function and perhaps to special stimulation in the same organ in the child. It may pave the way for choice of this particular organ for identification with the parent and later to its utilization by the conversion process as well as by symptoms which are designed to deal with conflicting impulses toward the identification figure. Instead of outward expression toward the object, both the impulses and the defense against them become internalized and disturb the function of the organ which has been so utilized.

This man's dramatic coaching served to hide his fury at his mother and other women for his subservience to them. Only his attempts to irritate the priests gave any hint of the intensity of his repressed rage which finally broke through during therapy in the transference, particularly when he was drunk. His larynx and his voice then became not only the symbol of the destructive sexual organ of his mother with which he attacked, but also the organ which was attacked in identification with his passive father.

His illness punished him also for his hostile wishes toward mother as well as his older brother. Finally, in Menninger's formulation (1938, pp. 88, 354-355), it represented a partial suicide, the sacrifice of an organ in order to preserve life and to forestall the total disruption which would represent the climax of his unconscious passive wishes.

Evidences of identification are ubiquitous. In our first patient arthritis appeared on the same side which had been involved in her mother's paralysis. In another patient, not previously mentioned, a double identification with both parents was clearly evident in both phases of a manic-depressive disorder. During depression the devalued ineffective parent became the outstanding identification, and was berated by that part of the ego identified with the dominant, efficient parent. In the manic phase this relationship was reversed.

It is impressive to note the great variation in intensity, tenacity, and susceptibility to treatment of the various symptoms related to identification. In the first patient, during certain stages of the conversion process the cycle could be interrupted. It is likely that hysterical identifications do not involve the ego as totally as those encountered, for example, in addictions or in psychotic depressions. In hysteria sufficient quantities of libido appear to remain available for object cathexis, whereas in the severe depressions libido seems almost totally taken up in the neutralization of destructive impulses and is unavailable for investment of objects. A patient who is so involved and so unable to love is also almost impossible to reach by therapeutic intervention.

The tenacity of the identification, or of the symptom derived from it, seems to depend on a number of factors: (1) the degree of ambivalence toward the objects, that is, the greater the ambivalence, the more tenaciously does the patient cling to the identification in terms of the symptom; (2) the period in which the original loss of the object took place; that is, the more primitive the organization of the ego at the time of the trauma, the more intense the degree of fixation; and (3) constitutional differences in the relative strengths of libido and mortido, in so far as these must influence the nature of the conversion process involved in identifications, as well as their amenability to therapy.

To paraphrase Freud's statement from "Mourning and Melancholia" (1917), that the shadow of former objects is cast on the ego, we may say in addition that the shadow of the former objects in terms of identification with them may then be seen in the dysfunction of organs which have become involved in the conversion process.

Finally some of the shifts in psychic energy involved in the course of identification should be considered.

In *The Ego and The Id* (1923c), Freud stated that the process of identification with father images, which are the precursors of the superego, has the character of desexualization or sublimation. During such a transformation defusion of instincts takes place, and the erotic components no longer have the power to bind completely the concomitant aggression which is thus freed for aggressive and destructive purposes. This recalls the fact that patients are frequently aware of the release of destructive energy at the moment of rejection or bereavement—a phenomenon which was referred to above and is often expressed as "I am dying." At this moment, libido is withdrawn from the object and reinvested in the body.

Freud (1924b) further postulated that the desexualization which occurs during the transformation of object into narcissistic libido, with renunciation of sexual aims, is the general route leading to sublimation. Possibly all sublimation is brought about through the mediation of the ego in such transformations of libido during the course of identification.

Hartmann (1955) accepts Freud's idea that sublimation of libido is a process by which the ego is provided with energy appropriate for its needs, and that ego energies are desexualized and not instinctual.

Hartmann believes that desaggressivized energy is equally as important as desexualized libido for the formation and function of the ego. Thus, neutralization is another alternative to aggression being turned outward, and in this sense self-preservation is in large measure an ego function dependent upon neutralization.

We note in the presented material the part played by identification in protecting the individual from self-destruction by suicide, by means of the process of neutralization of aggressive drives. The patient who developed a malignant growth in a hypercathected larynx which was also utilized as the organ symbol of various conflict-laden identifications beautifully illustrates Menninger's formulation of partial suicide, and the preservation of life by dint of sacrifice of an organ. Probably this is a frequent mechanism in many so-called psychosomatic syndromes.

8.

THE ROLE OF THE AGGRESSIVE DRIVES IN THE CONVERSION PROCESS

SAMUEL SILVERMAN, M.D.

The early psychoanalytic formulations of the relationship between the mental and the physical under conditions of repression stressed the role of the sexual drives—the libido. In the papers on the defense neuropsychoses Freud (1894, 1896) pointed out the role of conversion with reference to traumatic *sexual* experiences. He again emphasized the relationship of libido to physical processes in discussing hypochondria (1914b). Ferenczi (1919) also indicated in his paper on hysterical materialization how repressed libidinal drives find expression in an alteration of physical functioning, the involved organ being unconsciously used as a substitute for the genitals.

This initial emphasis on the role of libido tended to persist even after the theory of instincts had been reformulated to include the aggressive drives. Meanwhile, however, Cannon's work (1934) clearly established that anger and rage are accompanied by compensatory shifts in physical homeostasis. In addition, more and more investigators pointed out on a descriptive or phenomenological level the occurrence or predominance of hostility in patients with various types of physical disorders. A representative sampling of their findings is presented in the following summary.

Spasm of muscle and other dysfunctions of the musculo-skeletal system have long been associated with suppressed rage. Holmes and Wolff (1950) describe certain individuals whose skeletal muscles are in a state of sustained tension resulting in chronic and easy fatigability, and also sleep disturbances and anorexia. These individuals react to their environment as if it were a constant threat, and thus are continually hostile, either in an overt or repressed way. The "chemism" of anger is considered by Hayman (1941) to be unable to express itself through the muscular system in myasthenia gravis and does so in a deleterious way on other organ systems. Halliday (1937) suggested that the spasm, pain and rigidity of fibrositis represented an unconscious blocking of movements which represented symbolically destructive impulses. Recently Jonas (1951) postulated that during sleep the elimination of cortical control may lead to the utilization of the musculature to express aggressive impulses which are not goal-directed. The more pent-up the aggression, the more muscle groups may be activated which ordinarily are not a means of expressing aggressive feelings. Thus, under such circumstances, not only the muscles of the extremities are involved, but also facial muscles, eye muscles, vocal cord muscles, muscles of mastication, neck, spinal, diaphragmatic, intercostal, etc., muscles.

The skin also has been long recognized as a site for emergency discharge in states of anger and rage. Graham and Wolf (1950) feel that scratching in skin lesions represents hostility turned inward. Guilt and fear prevent the hostility from being discharged outwardly. They feel that this anger is most frequently activated by a mother figure who prohibits heterosexual activity. Klein (1949) emphasizes the role of aggression in dermatitis. Aggressive impulses are repressed because of a rigid superego. Scarborough (1948) felt that hostile impulses were the most prominent features present in patients with neurodermatitis. Woolhandler (1948) similarly noted that patients with neurodermatoses exhibited intense aggressiveness, practically precluding relaxation. Wittkower and Russell (1953) found in eczema patients that aggressiveness which was latent often led to onset or exacerbation of symptomatology. Similarly patients with pruritus vulvae and ani were found to have very powerful sadistic tendencies which often were handled by turning these impulses upon themselves via scratching. Patients with seborrheic dermatitis showed inhibited hostility.

Various investigators feel that hyperirritability of the heart and cardiovascular system is more commonly seen in connection with aggressive feelings and accompanying retaliatory fears than with sexual excitement. Patients with various heart arrhythmias were found by Duncan and Stevenson (1950) to have their cardiac episode when they were in situations which aroused their hostility. These patients were unable to discharge their hostile feelings in the usual ways. Gunther and Menninger (1939) report a case of a female patient who when examined genitally and rectally during physical examinations reacted with severe anxiety and extrasystoles. They felt that they were dealing with a person in whom the sexual act was strongly associated with unconscious hostile elements. They felt the sequence of events in the examinations to be an experimental repetition of a disturbed organic response to anxiety. Wolf (1947) cites the case of a female patient with nocturnal dyspnea which was related to unexpressed anger.

The importance of aggression in gastrointestinal disorders has been stressed by various authors. Zane (1947) emphasized that the conflict situation in peptic ulcer involved both fear and resentment. Marmor (1949) felt that aggressive impulses were a basic factor in this disease. Mucous colitis has been related to the presence of both strong anxiety and resentment, with the latter most frequently and strikingly noted in a psychological-medical study of sixty cases by White, Cobb, and Jones (1939).

These observations, though limited in scope, at least suggest that in many different organ systems of the body, physical dysfunction is in some way associated with disturbances in the discharge of aggressive drives.

It has been only in recent years that psychoanalytic literature has begun to include an increasing number of references to the influence of hostility on physical functioning.

Repressed hostility has been recognized as a factor in the development of arthritis. Lehn, Menninger, and Mayman (1950) feel that in this disease heightened aggressive impulses are turned inwardly in a self-destructive way, affecting the soma—particularly in the joints. The pain experienced acts to placate superego demands.

Miller (1942), in a psychological study of eczema and neurodermatitis, found that both his patients were extremely guilty about their hostility. This guilt was expiated through the medium of the skin lesions. In other words, the hostility was turned inward and expressed in a masochistic form upon the skin. Saul and Bernstein (1941) reporting on a patient with urticaria found that the chief reason she was so frustrated was due to guilt which in turn was due chiefly to hostilities against family figures. It was this which caused her masochism, which was seen in various aspects of her life as well as in her urticaria.

Alexander (1939) found that "chronic inhibited, aggressive, hostile impulses which appear in connection with anxiety have a specific influence upon the fluctuations of the blood pressure." He also stated that in hypertensives the aggressive feeling had no other outlets whereby they could be drained off. Saul (1939), in his study of seven psychoanalyzed cases of essential hypertension, noted as the basic psychological feature that both oral dependent wishes and hostile impulses were pent up and not accessible to discharge. Saul further described this hostility as chronic, intense, close to consciousness, inhibited but inadequately bound in an organized chronic neurosis. The hostility arose from conflict with a dominating parent, usually the mother toward whom there was an oral dependent attachment. Weiss (1940), reporting on cardiovascular lesions in arterial hypertension, stated that, in his cases, accumulated, unexpressed aggression reacted on the cardiovascular system. Schwartz (1940) described in detail his findings in an analyzed case of essential hypertension and concluded that the crucial point for the hypertension was hostile rebellion against masochistic submissiveness with consequent anxiety. The masochistic dependent attitudes were toward a dominating mother and internally to a rigid superego. The hostility developed as a rebellion against this submissiveness.

Bacon (1954) in her psychoanalytic observations on cardiac pain points out that this symptom occurs in patients who are being analyzed, when an acute conflict develops between receptive help-seeking drives and aggression accompanied by retaliatory fears. The aggression was both conscious and unconscious. Bacon further suggested that "intense oral impulses when accompanied by intense sympathetic stimulation resulting from rage or fear are the source of anginal pain in some instances." Oral impulses result in vagal stimulation, slowing of the heart, redistribution of blood supply, probable constriction of coronary arteries and arterioles. Disturbance of this anabolic type of circulation with vagal preponderance by sudden rage or fear, or both, results in increased sympathetic stimulation upsetting vegetative balance, causing a functional disturbance of the heart followed by ischemia and cardiac pain.

Fromm-Reichmann (1937) believed that just as voluntary muscle contraction could be an important sign of conscious hostility, so spasmodic contractions of involuntary smooth

muscles, especially in blood vessels, represented an unconscious expression of repressed hostility. This, she felt, was the
basic explanation for the symptoms in eight cases of migraine
which she studied. Such patients suffer from unresolved
ambivalence; they do to themselves what they want to do to
the ambivalently loved object. Sperling's observations (1952)
on migraine stress the intense narcissism of these patients,
which, when even slightly injured, provokes extreme rage,
requiring immediate discharge. However, repression prevents this, and subsequent pain and suffering are expressions
of guilt. An evaluation of psychic mechanisms in vasospastic
disorders of the hand has been made by Lowenhaupt (1952).
The main one is felt to be strong oral aggression, transferred
from mouth to hand. Richardson's patient (1955) with Raynaud's phenomenon and scleroderma affecting the hands
"recapitulated the death of a relative in the form of a slow
destruction of her own body, as if to expiate her guilt."

Respiration is markedly affected by rage; the panting
breath of the angry person is well known. Fenichel (1943)
describes some types of nervous coughing as being a substitute for and an equivalent of embarrassment or hostility.
The asthma attack was compared by Weiss (1923) to the
shrieking reaction of the infant when threatened with separation from the mother. The asthmatic is considered to reproduce this very early rage response to frustration. French,
Alexander, and Bacon (1941) equate the asthmatic attack
with a suppressed cry for the mother and emphasize the
asthmatic patient's dependency needs. Confessing or crying
often brings alleviation of symptoms in an attack. This would
indicate that strong guilt feelings associated with equally
strong hostile feelings toward the ambivalently loved object
have to some extent been relieved. In a recent paper, Bacon
(1956) presents a more specific discussion of aggressive impulses and their relationship to asthma. She states that clinical
evidence suggests that "asthma and other forms of respiratory

anxiety may be precipitated by nascent aggressive feelings involving anal, urethral, or sexual excretory impulses. Stimulation of the excretory mucous membranes by these fantasies sensitizes the respiratory mucous membranes. . . . The nascent excretory aggression arouses fears of excretory aggression from the outside world. The persons whom the patient has felt to be good he now expects to be bad and attack his respiratory apparatus in a talion manner, which responds psychologically as though it were really attacked by noxious substances." Deutsch (1951) points out that "in situations in which anger, rage or hatred cannot be acted out on the person in question, the breathing movements may take the place of the prohibited action. Respiration may then be accelerated or constricted or deepened." He further postulates that "there are individuals whose respiratory apparatus has become sensitized through sense perceptions . . . trigger mechanisms for the disturbance of the ego." In asthma, the panic of the ego which is caused by irreconcilable instinctual drives is expressed in the symptom complex of the disease.

Garma has described ulcer as an "internal digestive bite" due to remorse over oral aggressive wishes directed at the mother's frustrating breast. In a recent paper Garma (1957) states that ulcer is not due to a wish for alimentary well-being. Rather, it is closely related to an opposite masochistic wish to "swallow" the environment and childhood aggressions of the mother as if they were bad food. This disturbs digestive processes. Weisman (1956), in a study of six male patients with exacerbations of chronic duodenal ulcer, found that the basic affects were restrained resentment, angry guilt, and guilty fear. In these cases recurrence of symptomatology took place most often when the threat of depletion predominated over the promise of replenishment and the consequent angry protest was restrained.

In general, these investigations have stressed the importance of one or more of the following factors, in addition to that of repressed hostility, namely: (1) extreme narcissism, (2) a rigid superego, (3) heightened masochism, (4) marked ambivalence, and (5) strong pregenital orientation. However, the role of the ego in dealing with the aggressive drives, and the relationship of libido to the aggressive drives under these circumstances have been relatively unexplored, with the notable exception of Schur's article on the metapsychology of somatization (1955). In it he states that ego regression may result in both the ego's failure to neutralize aggression and a parallel resomatization of reactions. Earlier E. Bibring (1941) had pointed out in his review of the theory of instincts that, as Freud turned his attention more and more to the postulation of an independently subsistent instinct of aggression, the ego was thought of as being obliged to cope with aggressiveness just as it was obliged to deal with libido. "The ego, for instance, could give way to it, sublimate it, repress it, alter it by means of reactive formations, mitigate it by adding libidinal elements to it, or offer itself as an object and so direct aggression onto itself (perhaps via the superego)."

The energies associated with the aggressive drives may also be dealt with by the ego by the conversion process into some form of bodily expression. In this paper the circumstances will be discussed under which the conversion process takes place, using clinical data from the following analyzed case.

Mrs. X, a thirty-one-year-old graduate student, came into analysis because of increasing difficulties with her studies and with her marital adjustment. She had severe feelings of inferiority and was very hypersensitive and defensive in her relationships with people. She tended to be particularly competitive with men. In her dealings with authority figures she often developed disturbing feelings of anxiety and at times had fantasies of being attacked either verbally or physically. When she felt rejected or unable to advance in her work as quickly as she had hoped, she would have depressive moods. She was only infrequently aware of or able to give vent to her angry feelings. The patient's preoccupation with her body and state of physical health has been marked for many years. She tended to have many different physical symptoms, especially when she was under tension. She had had several surgical procedures prior to analysis. Some ten years ago following a miscarriage she developed left-sided abdominal pain and a year later a small polyp was removed from the descending colon; at the same time a hemorrhoidectomy was done. A few years later she had a hysterectomy. This occurred nine months after the birth of her last child. Numerous myomata were found in the uterus.

The patient was born in one of the Southern states and is the older of two girls. Her father was a philanderer and poor provider. The patient's mother led a very unhappy life with him and was often in poor health. As a child the patient was intensely jealous of her sister and was frequently at odds and fighting with her. She tended to be tomboyish and took poorly to household chores. She often felt rebellious toward her mother and frequently gave only lip service to her instructions. She was very much afraid of her father and tried to stay out of his way.

When the patient was twelve years old, her mother died of an acute lung infection. After the mother's death, the home was maintained with the help of various "housekeepers" and an aunt of the patient's. Some five years later the patient left to go to college through which she was financially helped by relatives. She did not return home and has not seen her father since. Her thoughts of him subsequently continued to be bitter and reproachful.

The patient worked for a while as a secretary and as a research assistant. Her first marriage was to a rather dominating, selfish, and inconsiderate man and ended in a divorce. Her second marriage was to a passive, effeminate man with whom she was often highly competitive and whom she tended frequently to devaluate. Several children were born, temporarily delaying the patient's plans for her graduate work. When she resumed her studies, she felt a conflict of interests between her work at home and at school. She felt her husband was getting far ahead of her in his career. At the same time she felt she was neglecting her children. Her relationships with her teachers were defensive and competitive. She frequently felt she would fail and her position would become even worse because her husband might leave her. It was at this point that she entered analysis.

During the early stages of analysis the patient remained ensconced behind the resistance of a pseudo compliance. She would talk without hesitation or overt blocking and gave an illusory impression that she was communicating freely by proceeding rapidly from one association to another. In effect this resulted only in "scattering" her thoughts, so that it was difficult to derive any theme or common denominator from the associations. Furthermore, she tended often to be highly descriptive and talked in a bland, monotonous tone of voice. She thus tried to avoid discovery of what she considered as "bad" in her thoughts and feelings—her "defects," her sexual and aggressive impulses, her competitiveness and rebelliousness. This was the way she had reacted to the authority figures in her past—by a pseudo compliance. Gradually the more openly negative aspects of the transference were revealed in her fantasies about the analyst, and there was associated acting out negatively toward her husband and occasionally toward her professors. Her husband appeared as a particular figure to be devaluated. The professors were seen principally as attackers and villains (all representing father figures). Though the content indirectly revealed extreme hostility, there was little affective expression of this during the hours. Projection and rationalization appeared early and prominently as defenses.

As the analysis proceeded beyond these early phases, the occurrence of and reference to physical symptoms became more frequent. The patient complained of abdominal and anal pain (sites of her previous operations). Headache was recurrent and severe. She had numerous sore throats and colds. As the patient brought up her physical symptomatology, its *painful* character was stressed—a way of communicating that she was suffering, although she did not talk directly about suffering. Most prominently, however, and from the very beginning of analysis, the patient connected her physical symptoms with fantasies about growths, particularly in her abdomen. These growths at times were associated with libidinal elements and then chiefly represented penis symbols. At other times the growths were also associated with thoughts of suffering and dying, and with guilty feelings. It was then that the patient recalled that her mother had always complained of having tumors within her. She had thought that one tumor was low in her mother's abdomen. However, she was quite certain of another tumor her mother had always had. This was a goitre. The patient had felt that it had always been difficult to know how sick her mother really was, because a doctor was never called until the mother's fatal chest illness.

On a number of occasions the patient also referred to the symptom of soreness in her left breast. Again the fear of a growth was associated with this symptom. She recalled that when her breasts were just starting to grow, they were similarly very sore and tender. She had been told that she was breast-fed but that her mother's milk supply was inadequate. She was colicky, very thin, and cried a great deal as a baby. She brought up fantasies that she was poisoned or starved as a baby and also had fantasies of biting at breasts. The patient's further associations about her childhood illnesses led her to recalling frequent attacks of tonsillitis with painful swellings in her throat; also the time she had mumps and was an object of ridicule. She was also suspected of having TB and had a number of chest examinations. Her sister was more sickly than she and thus received much more attention. There were repeated connections in the patient's associations about early illnesses and growths, defects, being neglected, hostility and suffering.

While physical symptoms occasionally appeared in connection with forbidden libidinal wishes, especially the need for a penis, less often for a breast, the development of the patient's somatic complaints during the analytic hours could be more closely and more frequently correlated with an intensification of hostile impulses and guilt as they were revealed indirectly in ideational content, usually without associated affect. This hostility was activated by current competitive situations with men or phallic women, and also particularly by feelings of frustration when dependency needs were increased and unsatisfied. Both reactions were reflected in the transference. During such times the patient's hostility was being converted and announced somatically.

The patient's aggressive drives appeared to be much more powerful and prominent than the libidinal drives. The patient had only occasional sexual relationships with her husband, relatively unsatisfactory, and sexual fantasies and memories were brought up rather infrequently with hesitation and much blocking. It was obvious that she had an intense penis envy, with a marked revenge type of the female castration complex. It was apparent quite early that the patient also had to struggle with a harsh and punitive superego.

A shifting emphasis on the conversion process, projection and rationalization, pseudo compliance, competitive drives with occasional discharge of anger, dependent and masochistic tendencies was noted. The patient might then have anxiety and/or mild depressive moods, or else she might be reacting with physical symptoms or minor illnesses—or she might be relatively free of these for brief periods.

During the first year and a half of analysis the clinical

picture was characterized by these shifts. Then the patient went through a number of major reality situations with serious repercussions. She had been studying quite hard for a final examination for her advanced degree. She had recurrent fantasies of her examiners as brutal men who would attack her and try to prevent her from passing. In these fantasies she anticipated usually that she would be overwhelmed; less often she triumphed over the attackers. The examination was seen as a kind of life-and-death situation—a major test of her adequacy as a person. The patient took and failed the examination, but was given an extension of time and another opportunity to take the examination within six months. She felt quite depressed and anxious. She thought of herself as irremediably defective and a failure. She felt she would not be able ever to have a career and would be forced as a housewife into a position of dependency, suffering, and sickness (like her mother). She attempted to combat her low spirits by devaluating her examiners and the analyst, and accusing them of having been inconsiderate and unfair. The intense hostility activated by this episode found, however, relatively brief outward discharge, despite attempts at working over the material during the analytic hours.

At about this time the patient's older child, a girl, developed a severe infection. The patient reacted to this with guilt, felt responsible for the sickness, and saw herself as the bad mother. In addition, she identified with the child, seeing its illness as a major defect and thus her own feelings of inadequacy were further intensified. However, the depressive mood soon subsided again.

Then followed a period of a month's absence from the analysis during the summer vacation. The patient reacted to this as if it were a desertion of her by the analyst with a deepening of the negative aspects of the transference. The content of her associations revealed frustration of dependency needs (already markedly enhanced by the prior events) and intensified hostility, though again affective expression was relatively blocked.

After the vacation period and resumption of treatment the patient's husband began to make plans to move the family outside the United States. This not only threatened the continuation of the patient's analysis, but also involved the possibility of her being located far from adequate medical care. Her fears that her husband did not care for her, and her feelings of frustration and dependency, and associated hostility continued to be further activated. It was obvious that under the impact of these successive events, enormous energies associated with the aggressive drives were being mobilized, and accumulating.

It was against this background that the patient began again to be preoccupied with the possibility that she had growths in her body and that she might die of cancer. There were further associated references to burning sensations in her left breast, which became the focus of her attention during a number of subsequent hours. Then a new symptom developed. The patient began to note pain in her right chest near the costal margin. She thought she had the grippe. Although the patient rarely actually looked at her body, despite her preoccupation with it (to avoid seeing the feared "defects"), she finally did so a few days after the onset of the pain and saw a small lump in her right breast, some distance above the area which was painful. She was immediately seen by her internist, who made a tentative diagnosis of benign tumor of the right breast. This was confirmed by her surgeon who advised immediate operation. At operation a frozen section revealed a small infiltration of adenocarcinoma. A radical mastectomy was then done. No metastases were found. Following several weeks of convalescence from the operation, the patient returned to analysis.

The patient's reactions initially were to feel more defective than ever before. At the same time there was a compensatory increase in her need to make up for her physical defect by intellectual means. The approaching re-examination for her advanced degree thus loomed all the more as a desperate life-and-death situation. There were also accompanying increased envious thoughts about the power and advantages which she assigned to men and a desire to deprive them of these. There appeared more openly and frequently sadistic fantasies of cutting men down physically, of lopping their heads off. The patient kept referring to her father in a very devaluating way, calling him a liar, dirty, and a deserter. After a brief interval the hostile content subsided, and the patient reverted to her earlier tendencies of scattering her associations and blocking off of affect. Thus the hostility was again turned inward, and the defense of not getting involved emotionally, not looking at herself, her body, her thoughts and feelings was again reinstituted. It also prevented others, especially the analyst (in father transference), from having a chance to scrutinize her in these respects.

In the meantime, preoccupation with physical symptoms continued, and grew even greater as the direct hostile content disappeared from her associations. There were frequent references to limitation of motion and weakness of the right upper extremity. Many thoughts concerned with lumps and growths were brought up. She complained of excessive intake of water and frequent urination. She kept referring to the possibility of having a lump in her intestines which was making her urinate excessively. She thought her bladder was becoming bigger and harder. The patient became now aware of her hostile competitiveness again and noted its relationship to the urge to urinate frequently. She recalled that she had been enuretic until puberty and did not menstruate until she was almost sixteen. As a child, being often afraid to be alone, she insisted on sleeping frequently with her mother. On a number of these occasions she would be enuretic, waking to find herself clasping her mother with her legs, having wet them both. Thoughts of the examination and the need to show her examiners up, to be better than they, again emerged in the material. At this time the patient made a remarkable statement about the relationship between her emotional state and physical condition: "I know that I have very strong competitive feelings about passing that examination at school and getting a good job. In people who have a tendency to grow things, it doesn't do to have these growths out as long as their psychological problems continue to make things worse. In me it's this feeling of defect and competitiveness, this need to get ahead of the men."

About two months after the mastectomy had been performed, and within a week after the appearance of the new symptomatology, the patient was again examined by her surgeon. He advised hospitalization for further studies and possible exploratory laparotomy.

The day before the patient was scheduled to go into the hospital she had an unusual number of associations about her hostility. She recalled how as a child she had frequently hated her parents and associated what she called her "criminality" with this hatred. She remembered how for a very brief period in childhood her temper would flare up and lead to violent and uncontrolled behavior, especially toward her mother. She would tell herself that by this behavior she could force her mother to stop trying to change her over. Shortly before the analytic hour she had actually had an outburst of very angry feelings toward an older woman friend who represented a mother figure to her. She had felt that this person had acted in a selfish and dominating way toward her. Shortly after the episode the patient felt depressed. She was able to note the obvious connection between her hostility and guilt feelings. She had the strong impression that she was paying for her hostility by becoming physically sick. She then recalled how her temper tantrums as a child had given way to a passive resistance toward her mother as she grew older. She was, however, so afraid of her father that she was never able to express her hostility to him directly until she was long in adolescence—and then only on a few occasions.

Shortly after re-entering the hospital, the patient was explored and a very large, ovarian cyst was found and removed. There were no physical complications postoperatively, and after several weeks of convalescence the patient again returned to analysis.

The first hours after her return were filled with references to the sadism of the doctors and nurses at the hospital toward her and other patients while in a helpless state. She identified herself with an acquaintance who had been recently killed by robbers. This person, a man, had been so arrogant and had acted with such overbearing superiority that many people who knew him had wished that something bad would happen to him. She equated her hospital experience with being tortured by bandits. This she saw as a punishment for her own feelings of arrogant superiority and devaluation of men, particularly her father. She had been hurt because she had been bad. She recalled her mother's admonitions: "Mother warned me about mean deeds or angry feelings—that I'd be sorry for them." There followed again a period of blocking which was marked by the presence of such physical symptoms as "stuffed up" head and constipation. The patient was able to note again and again how she was reacting physically when she was under tension, and when her thoughts and feelings, particularly the hostile ones, were blocked. The patient continued to show increasing awareness of her hostile feelings and an understanding of the intensity, extent, and meaning of her hostile thoughts. This "break-through" occurred some two and a half years after the start of the analysis and about a month after her second operation.

While there was a brief recurrence of preoccupation with physical symptoms—principally soreness in the left breast— the patient's anxiety level slowly decreased as she worked through this material. When the patient took her examination some months later, she actually did quite well and was praised by her professors for her good work. She had now fulfilled all the requirements for her advanced degree and was awarded this a few weeks later.

In reviewing the clinical data in this case, the following points seem worthy of special emphasis:

The patient's ego had to cope not only with drives in which the aggressive components were especially powerful, but also with a superego that was severely punitive, and, additionally, with environmental stresses of varying intensity. The patient reacted with particular sensitivity to situations which represented for her a desertion. This desertion could be outright, threatened, or implied. It could be represented by neglect, disappointment, attack, or abandonment. Under such circumstances, the ego, in attempting to cope with the activated aggression, utilized various mechanisms and combinations of mechanisms including projection, rationalization, identification, pseudo compliance, and competitive overactivity. From time to time the insufficiency of the ego's efforts led to states of depression mixed with anxiety. The ego also utilized the conversion process, marked by the appearance of physical symptoms. Was the conversion process also closely connected with the patient's physical diseases? In order to approach an answer to this question, it is necessary to examine in greater detail the conversion process itself and the role of the aggressive drives in this process.

This patient's analysis repeatedly indicated a close relationship between physical dysfunction and activated aggression turned inward. This relationship appears to have begun very early in the patient's life. She was brought up in an atmosphere of illness and martyrdom generated by her mother who had many symptoms referable to the throat, chest, and abdomen, but particularly complained of her growths. The patient herself was weaned abruptly early in the nursing period. She was a finicky eater, thin, colicky, was suspected of having TB, and had frequent sore throats and colds. As a child she showed hostility infrequently and openly only toward her sister. With the adults she was shy, never spoke up, was pseudo-compliant; she was particularly afraid of her father and did not cross him. The very early roots of the conversion process were again repeatedly revealed in the course of the analysis, especially in the transference neurosis, when hostility was blocked off from ideational and affective expression and was announced somatically in the sensitized body areas, through the appearance of various sensory perceptions, especially about the size, shape, and location of growths.

There were a number of closely related temporal correlations between the impact of later severe environmental stresses which mobilized intense aggression and the development of physical symptoms and physical disease. When the patient's first husband neglected her severely and in effect deserted her, the symptom of pain in the left side of the abdomen appeared together with marked constipation. Some months later a polyp of the colon and hemorrhoids were surgically removed. When her second husband withdrew from her following the birth of a child, the abdominal pain returned. When he repeated his behavior following the birth of the second child, the patient again had abdominal pain and a uterus studded with fibroids was removed.

Again, during the analysis, under the impact of successive events (already outlined) interpreted as desertions, attacks, and losses, enormous hostile energies were mobilized. These energies were for the most part turned inward. The patient at this time developed the growth in her right breast and a cyst in the abdomen.

It is interesting here to note the findings of Bacon, Renneker and Cutler (1952) in a psychosomatic survey of forty patients with cancer of the breast. These patients had among other characteristics (1) masochistic character structure, (2) inhibited sexuality, (3) inability to discharge or deal appropriately with hostility. These authors feel that one must consider an internalized self-destructive drive to be present in the cancer patient.

The case history which has been presented here may be considered also from another point of view. If the conversion process has among other adaptive measures been frequently used by the ego, it may become particularly prominent during periods of regression when the usual defensive constellations become insufficient. At such times the ego may fall back, as it were, to older methods of defense—and the conversion process represents a very early type of defense— perhaps a precursor of defense. If, at the same time, the capacity of the ego to sublimate (neutralize or desaggressivize) aggression is limited to begin with, and is still further reduced during periods of regression, this may set the stage for extensive defusion of the drives. When, through the conversion process, body parts are cathected with energies from the drives, there is interference with physical functioning. The more defused the drives, the greater the extent of interference with physical functioning because of the unmitigated destructive or catabolic potential released. The result may be noted in a range extending from transient physical symptoms to fully developed physical disease, depending on the degree of defusion and quantity of aggressive energy thus released. The turning inward of aggression is further enhanced when the ego, via a severe superego, offers itself as an object for the discharge of the aggression.

It is clear that the conversion process, and in particular the aggressive drives, stand in no simple relationship to the development of physical disease. The factors of heredity and development with respect to both the physical and mental apparatus and the later precipitating events which may be of decisive economic importance, all have to be considered.

9.

CONVERSION AS PROCESS AND CONVERSION AS SYMPTOM IN PSYCHOSIS

JAMES MANN, M.D. and
ELVIN V. SEMRAD, M.D.

A presumably ideal state of human existence would be one in which all human beings would live a physiologically correct life. By this we mean that, even with respect to individual constitutional differences, the physiological functioning of the human organism would be completely adequate and would serve, without digression, to achieve a total state of integration between the individual and his inner and outer environment. Thus, one would see what there is to be seen (perceive in full), feel what there is to be felt (accept fully one's perceptions), integrate all perceptions properly in accord with one's total experiences and then achieve definitive action which would assure adequate discharge of tension. In this process, the individual could live out, to its maximum, his genetic endowment since such endowment would then remain neither encumbered nor exhausted by essentially extraneous stress experiences.

The extraneous stress experiences, even though they achieve an existence through physiological processes, are considered extraneous in so far as, under other conditions, one could do without them. We think of these experiences as accompaniments of symbolizations; the process as the symbolic process and both process and symbol as the matrix of human psychological function. Early in life, physiologic sensations already have included, as part of their processes, specialized symbolic meanings which are unrelated to the specific organic function of the sensation itself. From this point of view, physiology and psychology are interwoven and continue through life in an inseparable state. The process of conversion of the physiologic cell-state into a physiologic-psychologic cell-state begins very early in life and is indica tive of a disturbing and disturbed process which, at some point, still early in the development of the individual, will begin to make itself manifest in end results which we will call conversion symptoms. The conversion process will be effective at the motility level, at the visceral level, and at the ego level. It is at the ego level that we shall consider the conversion process since our present state of knowledge permits a certain proficiency only in the realm of the clinically observable.

From this point of view, the term conversion process may be used to denote what has been generally called "psychosomatic" or "psychophysiologic," and the conversion process is considered to be universal in so far as excess excitation always alters physiological processes. Furthermore, we propose that the human being is organized on the prototype of a single cell which also functions on the pleasure-pain principle. It follows then that when a state of displeasure occurs, it is managed by the individual's reactive physiological structure linked with the sensation of distress so that, through repeated experiences of displeasure, cell modification ensues in which physiology becomes physiology-psychology. Whenever the cell responds physiologically, a response to a psychological stimulus is part of the total cell response. The opposite is also true. The question naturally arises as to how much affect the body can handle or manage or absorb? Is there an individual body capacity for such management of affect beyond which there arises the need for the observable defenses? In this connection, we note that the more immature of the ego defenses (the narcissistic defenses) are so much more "body-oriented" as compared to the more mature defenses. In the narcissistic defenses so much of the affect is concentrated upon the self to the marked exclusion of external objects. A reasonable assumption that follows is that the need for defenses is inversely proportional to the success with which the conversion process handles affect.

The link between physiology and psychology with regard to psychosis is best understood through consideration of the management of anxiety. Conversion, as a universal process, affects the organism at all levels of integration, including all levels of integration of those functions we know as the ego. The chief difference between psychosis and neurosis is essentially a question of time in so far as at a certain time in development, the ontogeny of the ego is affected and whether psychosis or neurosis will follow is determined by the resistance of the ego; whether the ego will be overwhelmed or whether the more mature, more adaptive, more complex mechanisms of defense will have developed and become solidly and effectively organized. This latter organization consists of patterns (1) for and as executant functions for interpersonal living, (2) as executant functions for and as expressions of physiological functioning, and (3) in all those processes that bring these together into harmonious union best serving the pleasure needs of the individual in accordance with reality.

Current scientific development arising from our clinical work is better versed in recognizing the executant functions involved in interpersonal functioning than are our somewhat obscure tools for studying physiological changes and their intimate relationships in the development of body ego. We stress that the psychotic ego is no different from any other ego except that the conversion process has exerted decisive influence and decisive effects earlier. Furthermore, because the conversion process begins with the earliest introjections of even minute aspects of the environment and in so far as this process aims at diminishing displeasure, then the development of defenses is synonymous with the process of conversion and the defenses themselves are conversions, the end results of the process.

A variety of psychiatric treatments may undo the conversion but only the penetrating work of analysis aimed at separating psychologic function from physiologic function may undo the conversion process by creating a transference relationship which presents an object to the patient instead of the internalized object or the self.

In the psychosis-vulnerable person, in relation to the conversion process, we are dealing with pregenital, preoedipal object problems. Early object relationships, part or total, flood the sensory organs from without and the responsive organism floods from within with positive pleasure sensations and/or negative painful sensations. The ambivalence, the quantitative distribution between the negative and the positive, is at least in part the answer to whether or not the early ego will be overwhelmed. Similarly, the physiological activity accompanying and being part of ego integration will share the same fate in the sense that the development of consistent physiological and psychological expression of a personality around a specific affect will depend, too, on whether or not the early ego is overwhelmed. Clinical evidence points to the opposite also occurring, namely, the early ego accompanying and sharing the fate of overwhelming physiological disturbances.

With negative feelings in the ascendancy, there will be interference with introjection, symbolization and ego-ideal identification. We believe that the interference occurs in the position of symbolization so that the symbol does not become a useful part of the superego as an ego-ideal identification but functions as a foreign body. In this position, there will be modification of physiological functioning at all levels of integration including the ego structure itself. In a case to be described in detail, a female schizophrenic, experiencing once more in psychotherapy this precise point of early ego aberration, told of her intense desire to swallow the therapist. This wish was acceptable to her but for the fact that she felt he would be promptly eliminated unchanged and covered with feces. The need to rid herself of an undesirable object was apparent. Later, when a friend called to inquire of her health, the patient responded completely spontaneously that she had been ill with colitis. The patient wondered why she had made such a response since she did not ordinarily have any special bowel symptoms.

At the ego level, identification would appear to follow the principles described by Anna Freud (1936), i.e., identification with the aggressor resulting in character traits relevantly related to the unconscious of the aggressor. In the psychotic, the aggressor may well be primarily a foreign body. The defensive nature of this kind of identification is clarified when one notes that the identification is not only with the aggressor and that identification with the aggressor is but part of the identification. The defensive system available to the ego at this point in its development, the narcissistic defenses, may also be affected in that they become intensified and specialized so as to emerge as a prominent executant series of patterns in the style of denial, projection and distortion. Such prominence seriously compromises the functioning ego in its interpersonal negotiations and eventually victimizes its owner by assuring frustration of his object needs.

Although the object of identification is experienced as an aggressor and perceived as a foreign body, the fact of ambivalence speaks for the presence, too, of a positive pleasure-giving source in this intensely symbiotic relationship. The positive pleasurable aspects become the source of supply and the major factor in balancing aggression, making it possible thereby for the ego to remain intact. This kind of stability is vulnerable and continues to be effective only until such time as the individual loses, realistically or otherwise, primary satisfying objects and/or, to a lesser extent, such secondary objects.

With this kind of loss, the previously balanced "poison" of the aggressor is liberated and the ego is confronted anew with the problem of containing and controlling aggression while libidinal problems assume a clear-cut secondary position. We might say that at this point the conversion symptom has failed, and the patient is once more thrown into the disorganizing and exhausting conversion process—a state of exquisite psychophysiologic pain—and must soon reach toward another solution. The solutions open to him at this point are three in number—suicide, murder, and/or the protective, economical and restitutive features of clinical psychosis. The total process may be acute and overwhelming or it may be slowly regressive. So it is that in acute psychotic reactions an invariable accompaniment to the distortions of the external world is a series of frightening, confusing and distorted body perceptions. For example, the body is cut in two; half the body is man and half woman; parts of the body are missing; feeling alive but dead; visceral disturbances and various intense visual, auditory and tactile sensations. The facts of loss of satisfying objects preceding the psychosis are verified by careful study of each psychotic patient.

Here it may be well to remark further on the specialized defenses of the psychosis-vulnerable person. We define the vulnerability as being due to the tenuous and delicate balance between ego-ideal identification and identification with the aggressor. This balance is maintained either by defensive ego specialization or by character disorder or by disorders of physiological functioning (or by organ dysfunction) in which symbolic expression is maximal and physiological expression important but not so clearly understood. In our clinical work, we see only the defensive organization of the ego and we recognize that the defensive specialization in the schizophrenic patient is in the realm of the narcissistic defenses now molded into organized patterns of denial, projection, and distortion. The ego is converted and altered in such a way as to operate in a self-consoling manner at the expense of either denying the presence of sensations, not acknowledging responsibility for sensations or not recognizing sensations from within or from without. Denial, projection, and distortion are themselves both altered ways and ways of altering sensory perceptions so that they may become ego-syntonic. Such specialization of the narcissistic defenses speaks for the inadequacy of ego-ideal identification and, as a consequence, varying degrees of serious loss of the capacity for repression. By contrast, the defensive organization of the ego in the affective disorders is in the area of what we call the affective defensive patterns. Here excessive compulsiveness, hypochondriasis and neurasthenia function as patterns of managing interpersonal relationships but not without considerable benefit from repression and sparing of perceptual abnormality.

The essential difference then between the unreliable defensive theme of the narcissistic disorders, namely denial, and the theme of the more successful defensive organization in the neuroses lies in repression. Visualized diagrammatically, this difference would consist of the number of associations (symbols) between impulses and repressive force. The greater the number of associations the greater the strength of the ego and this greater number is dependent upon the positively weighted quantitative distribution between positive and negative sensations as outlined above. (In other words, the better the mother-child relationship, the greater the possibility for a series of positive associations with respect to a particular important symbolic representation. In our schizophrenic patient, the opposite is true so that important symbols may very quickly flood the patient with immediate instinctual demands for discharge. In order to maintain some degree of integrity as a person, then a series of altered perceptions, i.e., narcissistic defenses, takes over.)

Looking at the effect of loss dynamically, loss results too readily in the supremacy of negative affects, thus dislocating the delicate balance between ego-ideal identification and identification with the aggressor. This kind of inundation necessitates regression to the point of deepest regression, the narcissistic position, where the patient is not only the victim but where he also operates for self-consolation. In this position, he achieves tension relief. (We know that chemical studies in schizophrenia indicate, if nothing specific, that widespread changes do occur. Can we regard these chemical changes as understandable dynamically in that the patient is as disturbed psychologically as a human being can become and still live. One might postulate that in the very acute disorganized psychotic reaction, the patient is literally boiling in the conversion process. In this cauldron, death may and occasionally does ensue but much more often, through his own means or through the application of external medical means, the process is interrupted so that *symptoms* may once more be installed. Homeostasis, however uneasy, is restored.)

The path of regression will vary according to whether the losses are acute and overwhelming or slowly cumulative. It will vary, too, in accordance with the type of structural organization in a given person. When the course of the present illness is plotted correctly, it is possible to demonstrate conclusively, especially in situations of chronic loss, an orderly progression of relinquishing of the more mature defensive patterns. We have already emphasized that the psychotic ego is different from any other ego only in that the conversion process has affected its development earlier with excess specialization in the infantile positions, consequent poor development and less reliance, therefore, on the more mature positions. This may account for the clinical confusion which speaks not only for many different kinds of mechanisms but also for many kinds of shading of clinical pictures which give rise to a confusion of terminology such as schizoaffective hysterical component, hypochondriacal component, neurasthenic component and more.

From this scheme it is possible to view and to understand more clearly the variations in schizophrenia which give rise to a spectrum of schizophrenic illness ranging from the hospitalized "very sick" schizophrenic, to the hospitalized "less sick" schizophrenic, to the so-called ambulant schizophrenic, to the rather completely concealed schizophrenic operating freely and perhaps quite successfully in society.

A married woman was first seen in 1951 when she was thirty-five years old. At that time, she complained of feelings of depression, vague fears, and of body odors which everyone knew must be coming from her. There were also suicidal suggestions which frightened the husband and led him to seek help for his wife. He himself had been treated briefly because of depression within the year.

The patient was an attractive woman with dark features who held her body, particularly her head, neck and shoulders, in a flexed position as though shrinking from the world and minimizing her size so as not to be seen. She could look at the analyst only for a fleeting moment and kept her head bowed almost continually. This symptom was to remain as a major resistance in treatment. At this time, she was somewhat blocked and vague but she was able nevertheless to convey a fairly clear story of what had been happening to her. In turn, it was possible to understand some of the factors productive of this first acute episode. The present illness was managed rather readily in psychotherapy and, because she had been functioning quite well as housewife, mother and social person, treatment was limited to goals which were moderately investigative but primarily supportive. Supportive here meant permitting the patient to use the warmth and understanding of the analyst to "mend her fences" and to return to reality. In three months, she had returned to her previous state of health and felt sufficiently well to refuse the suggestion that she consider psychoanalysis. In the years that followed, she was seen periodically, essentially on demand whenever anxiety increased to the point of threatened reappearance or actual appearance of bizarre sensations and ideas. With each return for help, further facets of her scheme of functioning became available for investigation. In April 1955, she was told that there would be an interruption for a year beginning in the autumn while the analyst was abroad and that a colleague would be available to her. This announcement appeared to provoke no special reaction beyond a modest and appropriate expression of regret. More than this was effectively denied.

The analyst returned in September 1956 and learned that the patient had seen the referred colleague very briefly and then had stopped with the remark that she would get along until her own doctor returned. The next contact came early in 1957 when the patient called to ask if it would be possible to begin an analysis. Told that time for analysis was not presently available, she insisted on waiting until she could be taken as an analysand. One week later, an urgent call from her husband made clear the emergent nature of her condition and she was seen the same night in a state of acute psychosis. It seemed as though the combination of past and present losses had become so interwoven with her experiences of sporadic and then prolonged loss of her analyst as to have provoked the most acute and deepest regression in her life. Treatment in the preceding years had served to bring to light the lifetime course of her development and the assaults upon her kind of ego sufficient to provoke brief and moderately severe periods of decompensation. Study and treatment at this particular period of disorganization clarified the story of her psychosis. What follows then, in chronological sequence, are the highlights of the nature of her illness. The data selected serve to illustrate the theoretic considerations presented above.

Born into a well-to-do family, she was the second of three daughters. One sister was eight years older and the other three years younger. With the older sister clearly representing mother, the patient's relationship was always defensively distant and consciously antagonistic with only intimations that warmth was also present. This sister often told the patient that she had not been wanted and was to be thrown into the river only to be saved by the sister.

The patient's feelings about her mother were more typically ambivalent in that while she considered mother to be a good woman, nevertheless mother was excessively critical of the patient and was so frequently away on trips as to make the patient feel that mother was not there for her. She considered her father to be a strong, omnipotent man who was never wrong. He was always frightening to her and although she felt that there was some way of tapping his warmth, her fear of him thwarted her efforts in this regard. She recalled, at the age of four or five, running with glee into her father's outstretched arms and accidentally dislodging his eyeglasses so that they fell to the floor. He reacted with enormous fury and she never yielded to him in this way again. It was her feeling that she was the least desirable of the children and was convinced that her parents concurred in their references to her as a "devil" and as an impossible child. Her earliest memories of herself carry a repeated theme of her own badness and lack of self-esteem. This unwanted, unloved feeling was further intensified in that much of her care, in contrast to her sisters, was entrusted to a nursemaid. She loved this nursemaid because "she loved me—she would sit me on her lap and it was warm and good—she was all that I had."

In this setting, she grew up as a somewhat isolated child, never feeling herself fully accepted or acceptable anywhere. She was apt to have but one friend at a time and made strong efforts to appear to be something more than she really felt herself to be. Thus she tried to be extremely "nice" to everyone about her. Wishing to be liked, she could not permit herself to say "no" to anyone. She denied that she was hurt by rebuffs and denied that she had any feelings other than "good ones." Her potential ability was never realized in school and it appeared that much of this failure was attributable to a school phobia which plagued her throughout grammar school and into high school. Never yielding to it sufficiently to stay out of school (that would mean being too bad a girl), it nevertheless preoccupied her to the point of distraction. She would watch the school clock under a growing wave of panic as she fantasied that if she did not go home soon, she would find her mother dead. She would run home and be vastly relieved to find that the dreaded thing had not happened. In high school, she had only one very close girl friend and she died of leukemia several years out of high school. The patient admired certains boys in her classes and wished very much to be close to them. It was her conviction, however, that the boys she wanted would never want her and that she would have to settle for those she considered much less desirable.

When she was fifteen, her mother's chronic pulmonary disease became worse and she took to her bed. One afternoon, the patient went out to do some shopping for herself and when she returned was horror-stricken to learn that in the interim her mother had been taken to a hospital and had died. She never ceased to blame herself for her mother's death. The combination of bad thoughts about her mother,

her selfishness in seeking for her own needs when her mother was ill and leaving her mother were sufficient to kill her. Nevertheless, she did not recall undue grief and remembered bursting into tears only once as she sat alone on the stairway in their home flooded with the sudden feeling of being alone and bereft.

While still in high school, she went out on a date and returned long past her usual hour. Her father was waiting for her, bitterly condemned her as a "whore" and refused her entrance to the house. For several hours, she wandered aimlessly and terrified in the dark streets and turned back finally in tearful desperation to be admitted to her home. There is no reason to doubt her innocence in the incident.

By the time high school neared its end, future goals and ambitions had failed to crystallize. A desire for college was only a gesture in favor of what her classmates were planning. In this, she was torn between the wish to "make a break" by enrolling at a distant college and the wish of her family that she go to a local school. She compromised by going to a dreary, rigid finishing school some thirty miles from home. There she felt more desolate than ever, felt accused of all kinds of violations of rules and quit.

At age nineteen, she married out of her feeling that she had better take the first opportunity offered to her since she could expect nothing of her choice. The marriage has always been comfortable economically and her husband has been kind and attentive to her needs. However, she has always felt that while he was the best she could get he was uncultured, insensitive and really beneath her. She characterized her husband as a weak, passive man whose success in business constantly amazed her. Actually, this concept of her husband applies to all men and is indicative of her enormous need to devaluate men. In her marriage, there emerge both the neurotic as well as the psychotic aspects of her personality. Seductive and flirtatious, she has always longed to possess sexually all men whom she recognized to be "strong." Conscious fantasies of size of penis and fellatio excited her more than they frightened her. She would feel her eyes inexorably drawn to the trousers of men who attracted her. Only guilt deriving from as yet unconscious destructive incorporative fantasies kept her from fulfillment of her seductions. In many other attitudes she displayed her derogation of the female role and her wish to be a man.

Four years after marriage she had her first child, a son. She felt very well during pregnancy and was delighted to have a boy. He was hers in every detail. She looked back in surprise at her capacity for infinite patience and love for him when he was an infant. With massive guilt she recalled admiring his penis, fondling it and, at times, mouthing it. She felt fulfilled and continued to feel so as long as the boy was small enough to serve her needs passively. Four years after his birth, she became pregnant again. The circumstances of this pregnancy are directly related to her overt psychosis. While she and her husband had talked about having another child, events forced a decision upon her. Her father died of cancer and several weeks later she was pregnant. In general, the atmosphere was unpleasant for the patient not only because her father had been lost so recently but also because she could not resist pressure to become pregnant so that the unborn child would also become heir to a particular legacy willed by the father. During this pregnancy she accompanied her husband on a business trip, and while alone in their hotel, was visited by a male acquaintance. She could not account for what followed except that while her intention had been to have intercourse the visit culminated in fellatio.

What had actually occurred was that illness had already descended upon her and she had felt consciously that the man with her was her father. Her reaction was one of profound horror, guilt, and degradation. From this point on she was never certain whether the baby was her husband's or her father's even though she could always intellectually assure herself of the facts.

In this state of mind, she eventually entered the hospital for delivery and remembered that, from the moment of entry, she began to cough ceaselessly. She recalled that her mother was said to have had silicosis and always coughed. "Mother always coughed and ever since I'm annoyed when anyone coughs." Her next recollection was that four days later her baby girl was brought to her. First she feared she might drop the infant and then was aware that she did not wish to have her at all. In the years that followed she was never able to forget the affair in the hotel.

For the next five years, she managed her life fairly uneventfully. Sexual relations with her husband were frightening to her and she compensated for this disappointment with an active fantasy life, interest in her son and a reasonably successful social and community life. A major portion of her social and community activity was motivated by the wish that somewhere, sometime in these outside contacts she might find the elusive something which would give meaning to herself and to her life. Significantly, she was always aware that when she was with people important to her, she would quickly adjust her mood to that of the particular person. In such relationships she came to be dependent on cues from others as to how she should be feeling. Compulsively clean in her household, perfectionistic in her demands upon herself and her family, substitutively good in her dealings with others, seductive and flirtatious with even a flair for the dramatic, she was constantly astonished to find that many people liked her as her patterns of defense operated more successfully in the eyes of others than in her own. Coursing through all her functioning were the massive element of denial and an almost total inability to know what she really felt at any particular moment. Feelings were strange, alien, and unrecognizable.

The beginning of the weakening of her more mature defenses began in the six months preceding her first visit for help. A loss had been going on which she had been able to deny successfully until confronted by even more powerful and more apparent evidence of loss. Her daughter, now five years old, had started school and was unable to go after the first few sessions because of a severe phobia. The mere fact of her daughter reaching school age was a serious blow in so far as it meant to the patient that both her children were needing her less and less as they grew up. Their growing independence separated them from her and this constituted an intolerable loss which left her empty, alone, and frightened. There was also present the masochistic need to keep near her as part of her at all times, the evil representation of herself in the daughter. The addition of the phobia brought into her adult life the repetition of her own childhood situation. Her daughter was being split off and confusion lay in the identification of the child not only as her own evil childhood self but also as her own mother. Repression began to fail once more and conscious wishes to destroy the daughter emerged in a setting of great anger and equal fear. Regression to the narcissistic defenses followed in a progressive manner. The neurotic defenses noted above disappeared one by one. She lost interest in the masculine-feminine struggle and concomitantly withdrew from the social scene. She became slovenly in her personal habits and in her home. She found herself wearing underclothing for weeks; later even her dresses remained unchanged for prolonged periods. The sight of her bed and its linens gave rise to sensations of disgust and bad odors. The storekeeper looking at her could see something about her and in her was foul and she averted her gaze. People could detect a stench from her body and there were "crabs" (pediculi pubis) wherever she had hair. Her appearance began to change in her own eyes and she became ever more uncertain as to how to translate and understand even insignificant stimuli in her environment. The impulse to destroy her daughter flared through regularly and served to intensify the variety of strange sensations that were developing. At this point, she was seen for the first time.

Between her first visit and the profound psychosis some six years later, a general retrenchment on a lower level of functioning had become solidified. Social relations and community activities were reduced in number and even these placed so much strain upon her limited and weakened defenses as to become exhausting after each event. Denial and distortion had become so strengthened as to make her completely unknowing of what she saw and felt. So arranged, she could walk through social and communal situations as if she were in utter control of herself and the situation. Thus even in the week prior to her acute breakdown, she continued to work as a volunteer in the pediatric section of a general hospital and there a fellow volunteer remarked that the patient always seemed to be the most composed among the harried female volunteer group. Significantly, she had maneuvered herself into work away from the patients because the constant exposure to numbers of defective children, many at death's door, brought too close to awareness her own feelings of defect and even more her own destructive impulses.

One month before the acute decompensation, the patient's old nursemaid had died. She felt some sadness and attended the funeral but shed no tears. Again she walked through the situation; she could not tell just why she went to the funeral. At the same time, her husband announced that he was going to send their daughter to a private school the next semester. This would mean that she would not come home for lunch and would return home later than usual. Furthermore, it might become desirable for her to board at the school during the week. (It should be noted here that six years before, while the mother was in treatment, the daughter was referred to a child psychiatrist and made a good recovery from her school phobia.) This announcement struck terror in the patient. She had to keep her daughter near her in order to assure herself of both her own intactness as well as that of the daughter. Daughter, mother, and grandmother were all one. To contribute still further, the husband also informed the patient that he had completed plans for the two of them to go on their long wished-for trip abroad. To this were added rekindled anger and fear with respect to the going away of the analyst. The words "going away" are in themselves sufficient to trigger collapse of defenses. In these words a variety of symbolic meanings are contained including guilt with regard to oral-incorporative fantasies, magical fulfillment of death wishes, and abandonment as an undesirable and unwanted child. These may be all subsumed under the one heading of "loss."

In this concatenation of events, uncontrolled anxiety and awful dread signaled impending doom. She began to take a variety of ataractics but felt no relief. The sense of something terrible happening to her increased and then came confusion and extreme agitation. At this point, she returned to treatment.

"Something is happening to me and I don't know what it is except that it is terrible." She was uncertain of what she saw, thought, and felt. "Am I half man and half woman"? "My body and skin feel strange and unknown to me." She feared she might kill her daughter or herself; her eyes pleaded for protection as she told of knowing nothing but the fear and terrible compulsion to kill. Agitation and sheer terror predominated.

Her defensive system had crumbled and she was caught up in free-floating terror (anxiety is too mild a term in this instance). Confusion was evident on all levels of ego integration (or disintegration) and no restitutive process was yet in operation. She was in the midst of an acute, overwhelming psychotic reaction in which unbridled aggression clamored for direct discharge. The victims were to be the aggressor in herself and the representation of the aggressor in the daughter. Husband and son were excluded from consideration.

In the next thirty-six hours, there followed heightened panic, loss of further defenses, and, for the first time, the total breakdown of denial. In the therapeutic relationship, the dissolution of denial had a positive aspect. She now told of her awareness of being full of hatred and, more than that, she was able to recognize the feeling of hatred within her. She knew and felt the desire to kill the analyst and everyone around her. This knowledge was accompanied by the sensation of being totally defenseless. She voiced, desperately and hopelessly, the dilemma of the schizophrenic, the essence of the early symbiotic relationship, "I hate you, I hate you, I hate you—and I need you."

In subsequent interviews, panic subsided as she felt more of positive sensations toward the analyst. She had begun to take in something good. Three weeks after the onset of this acute illness, at a time when compensation was still in process, the analyst had to leave the city for three days and the patient was referred to the same colleague noted earlier. During this absence, she had to see the colleague every day in order, as she expressed it, to hold on to the analyst through him and thus to suffer the loss without yielding to aggressive impulses and another dissolution. This kind of holding on became visible as a positive incorporative step. Always ambivalent, she then experienced, for days, the sensation of something in her throat which was choking her but which also tasted good. The object in her throat was the analyst and the wish was to eat him up. "If I could eat you up then I would have you inside of me and that would be good." When operating less psychotically, her interest would return again to fellatio with the analyst again becoming a transference father figure. Out of these sadistic, oral incorporative fantasies emerged the union with the aggressor, enormous guilt, self-blame and the concept of the evil and foul child. With the analyst offering more of "good object" then previously available to her, there followed some amelioration of the negative components and guilt changed its expression into a sense of execrable shame. She began to giggle, hang her head and hide her face in a manner wholly suggestive of an adolescent. The good incorporated object, however, would be lost sooner or later and so it would be both a good and bad object. Thus, after telling of her wish to eat the analyst, she added, "Unfortunately, I also thought that it wouldn't last long because you would leave me very soon." The exit would be via the bowel. In this connection, she told of a conviction (always close to consciousness) that people important to her, i.e., husband, children, self, and analyst were born covered with feces. Noted here is another example of the remarkable degree of unconscious communication between patient and daughter. At the height of the patient's concern with an object in her throat, the daughter became acutely ill with vomiting and diarrhea. As the mother's preoccupation diminished, the daughter quickly recovered and returned to school. The patient frequently stated that she always felt her daughter understood perfectly anything that the patient was experiencing. At an earlier period in treatment, when the patient was engrossed with the wish to be away from her husband, it was her then eight-year-old daughter who took to disappearing from home each day until long after dark. On one such occasion, the girl was found late at night hiding in the bedroom closet of a friend.

The process of incorporating the positive object continued for months with only occasional evidences of true transference phenomena as manifestations of higher ego activity. Four months after onset, the analyst left the city for a week. During this week of separation and loss, she experienced swings from elation to depression. She enjoyed her ability to recognize real feelings of love and anger. She found herself very much preoccupied with comments made in previous months by the analyst and remarked on her recollection of them with unusual clarity and understanding. To her surprise, many of the recalled remarks when uttered had been heard by her in a hazy, uncertain manner. She "spoke" with the analyst throughout the week and the feeling of love would change to anger when she felt she needed him and he was not there. Although absent, the analyst was with her in more of a positive than a negative sense. The loss, rather than provoking murderous wishes, now aroused a more integrated type of anger so that she felt people were "bitches and bastards" although these same people could be quite lovable at other times.

On the more regressive side, during that same week, there were short-lived episodes of confusion and gross distortion. These too were of a higher order in that the confusion and distortion revolved about the issue of her sex. When she saw the analyst on his return, at one point in the session, negative sensations began to mount. She became very much frightened and expressed the fear that she was "moving away" from him. One could almost see the ego crumbling as the patient had moved into a confronted situation of loss which suddenly mobilized such intensely guilty destructive fantasies as to force defensive retreat. With several quick and pointed interpretations along with the physical movement of drawing much nearer to the chair of the patient, she soon felt better and stopped retreating. Then came a feeling of comfort but also of sadness and, for the first time in some six years of relationship, she cried.

Treatment continues and this presentation will be concluded with further relevant data for the purpose of illustration.

"Instead of feeling, I have physical symptoms." This was said in the following connections. As transference reactions made their appearance, the analyst was at times the mother or the father. When experienced as father, the danger was always present that positive feelings of warmth and love would become intensified under the frustration of the therapeutic relationship to the point of rising aggression which, in turn, would promote the reappearance of sexual-aggressive oral fantasies. Resultant massive guilt would then induce the process of further defensive regression. At this point, the intensification of ambivalence would rapidly disintegrate her capacity to recognize feelings as abstractions and physical expressions became concrete expressions of feelings. Anger and guilt would become known only as a sensation of "burning" felt in the upper arms, upper back, and chest. Recently, under the impact of the problem of middle-aged emptiness arising out of the greatly lessened need of her children for her and the concomitant improvement in her general condition, there has appeared the wish to have a baby again countered defensively by the impulse to return to the situation of a baby herself rather than to struggle for new and adult satisfactions. As a result, she began to vacillate between threatened psychotic regression and successful mature moves. The nature of the conflict was crystallized, at one time, in her wish to purchase a new rug. Her old threadbare rug, she felt, was much too characteristic of herself. She chose one which she felt was the loveliest ever seen. When it was laid in her home, she became frantic with anxiety and collapse was in the offing. After much struggle, she gave up and returned the rug to the store. The rug was full of valued floral designs which represented youth, children, and having children.

In the many years that she has spent summers by the sea, she has remained fascinated with the sea anemone as it lies attached to a rock, "with its mouth opening and closing." This is the kind of attachment she seeks and, in regressed moments, experiences warm feelings not as such but rather as a sensation of her "stomach opening up"—and cold, angry, frightening feelings as the "stomach closing." These are felt in the literal sense. In her attempt to find adult substitute interests, she enrolled at a local university in a course in physical anthropology. She found this to be most interesting and gratifying.

A stabilized transference situation has not yet developed and this is probably due to the continuing fluctuations in the ambivalence felt toward the viscerally experienced analyst object. The image of the analyst as father or mother varies within the treatment session. When she can master her guilt with regard to the analyst as father, she is warm, alert, comfortable, charming and easily moved to a greater appreciation of her conflicts and of her assets. When overcome by guilt, she regresses rapidly, is unable to differentiate the analyst and moved quickly to preoedipal, pregenital defensive positions.

More recently, the mounting desire to have a baby again rekindled guilt-ridden destructive fantasies, and another episode of rapid regression ensued. As she plunged into the state of free-floating terror, she verbalized her status as follows:

"This time I feel everything physically—it is as though I am being reborn—everything is running through me like waves—not waves of water but like waves of diarrhea sweeping through my whole body—my skin burns more than ever —I feel like I am about to die—." Rupture of ego boundaries was experienced as general and particular sensations of pain without reference to external objects. Internal and external stimuli were felt only physiologically.

A major difficulty in treatment lies in her inability to alter certain frightening symbols which demand immediate discharge of aggression when experienced. There is hope that further progress may be made, however, inasmuch as she becomes more and more aware of how the symbol produces physical sensations instead of particular feelings. As a result, signs of mastery via greater strength of the positive transference with concomitant greater supplies of "good object" begin to appear.

Summary: We have presented a concept of the conversion process both from the theoretical aspect and from the aspect of the incorporation of this theory into the understanding of the nature of psychosis as observed clinically. Our aim has been to demonstrate that psychosis, and schizophrenia in particular, is a psychophysiologic entity. Further, we have attempted to clarify a point of view which will give broader and greater significance to the concept psychosomatic by approaching the question of psychosis through an examination of the conversion process as the pathway which might best illuminate the dynamic interrelationship of mind and body. By considering psychosis as a defect in ego development, by considering ego development as the observable consequences of the conversion process and by understanding the conversion process to be universal, we have sought to bring for further investigation, a unified concept of psychophysiological functioning from the special point of view of the psychosis.

10.

PSYCHOBIOLOGIC STUDY OF THE CONVERSION PROCESS IN WOMEN

DORIS MENZER-BENARON, M.D.[1]

This paper represents an attempt to describe and discuss certain aspects of the conversion process affecting the menstrual cycle in women. The material presented was obtained through psychoanalysis of patients suffering from either amenorrhea, anovulatory bleeding, premenstrual tension, or dysmenorrhea. Concurrent with the psychological study, urinary indices of pituitary-ovarian and of pituitary-adrenal activity were observed at regular intervals to provide a basis for correlation with phases of the transference neurosis.

PHYSIOLOGICAL BACKGROUND

The essential endocrine interrelationships of the menstrual cycle and pituitary-adrenal axis will be briefly reviewed.

Review of Pituitary-Ovarian Relationship during Menstrual Cycle

Every month during the reproductive phase of a woman's life, menstrual bleeding occurs as a result of the correct

[1] I am indebted to Dr. Somers H. Sturgis, gynecologist-in-chief, Peter Bent Brigham Hospital, for his direction of the gynecological and endocrinologic aspects of this study.
This work was aided by a grant from the Commonwealth Fund.

interplay of pituitary and ovarian hormones. The cyclic pattern of activity between pituitary, ovary, and uterus produces a rhythm that may vary considerably in different individuals, but that may be, for schematic purposes, represented by a cycle of twenty-eight days.

Two anterior pituitary gonadotropins[2] and two ovarian steroids are involved in the periodic occurrence of menstruation. The pituitary contributes follicle-stimulating hormones (FSH), and luteinizing hormones (LH). The ovary secretes two steroids, estrogen and progesterone. The latter is excreted in the urine as pregnanediol. The endometrium, stimulated by the two ovarian steroids, undergoes its cycle of proliferation, differentiation, and desquamation. Whenever the blood levels of either estrogen alone (anovulatory bleeding) or both estrogen and progesterone together (ovulatory bleeding) are substantially reduced, the endometrium breaks down and uterine bleeding occurs.

Up to puberty, ovarian follicles are constantly developed to a certain stage—then they regress and become atretic. Primary factors responsible for the menarche are not definitely known. It may result from an increased output of FSH or an increased maturity and sensitivity of the ovarian follicles to the previous level of FSH, which has been present through the first decade of life. Eventually one or more follicles produces enough estrogen to cause proliferation of the endometrium. It has been proved in some recent studies that atresia sets in, and owing to consequent depletion of hormonal support the endometrium breaks down with resultant bleeding (anovulatory bleeding). Existing evidence points to the fact that the proper hormonal balance of the mature cycle will generally not become established for several months after the first menstrual flow.

It is customary to name the first day of bleeding of the

---

[2] Luteotropin (LTH), a third gonadotropin, is not important for the purposes of the present discussion.

adult menstrual cycle day 1, when production of FSH is maximal and production of estrogen low. This converse relationship between FSH and estrogen levels is maintained as a basic principle throughout the cycle. Because of the strong FSH stimulation, a number of follicles grow and there is an increase in estrogen production on day 4 and day 5. By this time endometrial desquamation is completed. Epithelial proliferation coincides with further increase in estrogen production. Most follicles then degenerate into atretic follicles— usually only one follicle continues to grow to the mature graafian follicle which ovulates and ruptures on day 14. With the increase in estrogen secretion through the first half of the cycle, FSH secretion decreases. The endometrium responds with a rapid growth of all elements (proliferative phase). An augmented output of LH goes together with the estrogenic tide of the proliferative phase and is assumed to produce the endocrine trigger mechanism for ovulation of the mature follicle on day 14. After ovulation, the estrogen level drops slightly and the ruptured follicle begins to develop into the corpus luteum. The lutein cells accelerate progesterone production with the well-known differentiating effect on the endometrium (secretory phase). The LH output decreases at that point of the cycle. By day 20, the estrogen level is usually as high as just before ovulation and the progesterone level reaches its peak. It appears probable that a reciprocal relationship exists between progesterone and LH similar to that between estrogen and FSH. At the height of corpus luteum function, both pituitary gonadotropins are produced in minimal quantities. Under the influence of estrogen and progesterone, growth and secretory activity of the endometrium progress through day 25 and day 26. Unless at that time a fertilized ovum has implanted itself, degeneration of the corpus luteum is initiated. With the consequent falling of both estrogen and progesterone, changes occur in the endometrium that lead to menstrual bleeding. By day 28 the pituitary, now relieved from inhibitive levels of estrogen, starts again and rapidly reaches its peak of FSH output, which stimulates a new group of primary follicles for the next cycle.

Review of Pituitary-Adrenal Functions

Under normal circumstances the secretory activities of the adrenal cortex appear to be rather constant and at a relatively low level, in comparison with the great activity which follows upon any adverse changes in the external or internal environmental situation to which the individual must adjust. Increased adrenocortical activity can be in response to depression of circulating steroids and leads directly to increased pituitary secretion of ACTH. In addition, however, increased ACTH production can be governed indirectly by the sympathetic nervous system. An immediate increase of epinephrine will produce a deficit of carbohydrate reserves and considerable loss of water and electrolytes. This condition will also result in increased ACTH production.

In contrast to epinephrine and sympathetic nervous system stimulation which accelerates the utilization of the store of immediately available carbohydrates in the form of glycogen and results in the loss of electrolytes and water during the early phases of the response to stress, the adrenal corticoids produced by stimulation of the adrenal cortex by ACTH on the other hand increase the utilization of fat as a source of energy, either directly or by conversion to liver glycogen. Furthermore, through the action of the adrenal corticoids on the sweat glands and renal tubules, sodium and water are retained to replenish body fluids. The adrenal-cortical hormones thus counterbalance the effects of the early mobilization and utilization of immediately available energy reserves in the first phase of the response to stress.

Continued sympathetico-adrenal-medullary excitation, resulting from continued exposure to stress, may lead to prolonged high level secretion of ACTH through hypothalamus-pituitary stimulation.

The metabolic and physiologic effects of adrenal-cortical stimulation by ACTH suggest that three different general types of hormones may be secreted by the adrenal gland:

1. Compound F-like steroids such as 17-hydroxycorticosterone and Compound B or corticosterone.
2. 11-desoxycorticosterone-like compounds, such as 11-desoxycorticosterone and Compound S (11-desoxy-17-hydroxycorticosterone).
3. Androgen-like steroids such as adrenosterone.

Some Definitions

Functional dysmenorrhea is defined as a painful reaction to menstruation severe enough to interfere with a person's regular activity, in spite of palliative medical treatment. It is associated with the normal occurrence of ovulation and ensuing secretion of progesterone. It does not occur in anovulatory cycles.

Premenstrual tension, like dysmenorrhea, is associated with the occurrence of ovulation and secretion of progesterone. The symptoms include a series of physical and emotional disturbances consisting of water retention, painful bloating, and swelling of the breasts. Emotional disturbances are shown by uncontrollable mood swings, fluctuating between rage and depression together with accompanying primitive thought processes. With onset of menstrual flow, there usually is a dramatic relief of the organic and emotional disturbance.

Hypothalamic amenorrhea is defined as infrequent or absent menses due to the failure of LH and progesterone secretion resulting from emotional conflicts. In these patients, FSH is usually within normal limits. There is also failure to respond with bleeding to progesterone injections. In contrast to dysmenorrhea or premenstrual tension, patients with hypothalamic amenorrhea temporarily or permanently fail to ovulate and thus, to menstruate.

REVIEW OF LITERATURE

Helene Deutsch (1944) discusses the psychological task of the pubescent girl in facing the biological changes of the menarche. In connection with the bleeding, ideas referring to the female castration complex are revived with fantasies concerning injury and death. Together with this, the repressed hatred of the menstruating "witch-mother" endowed with magical powers, comes to the fore, leading to an increased aggression against her. This accounts for the expectation of menstruation as a threat. This aggression produces guilt feelings and may be turned against the self. Because of the biological processes, sexual drives increase, leading to an intensive struggle against masturbation, also associated with a sense of guilt. The reaction to the first period depends on the psychological maturity of the individual girl.

In girls not advanced beyond prepuberty, bleeding usually represents eliminatory functions associated with the cloaca theory. This reaction is particularly strong in girls with a history of enuresis or enteritis during childhood. The first menses then represents a lack of control over body fluids coinciding with the feeling of lack of control over aggression with the same resulting shame and guilt.

In girls with a marked castration complex, there may be an attitude of denial to the first menses, with the major effort directed toward a symbolic restoration of the male genital. All pubescent girls are faced with the conflict engendered by a biologically increased sexual drive and an increased psychological resistance against its gratification. If the genital trauma cannot be mastered through an increase in narcissism and a normal feminine fantasy life, masturbation will usually increase. If this is the case, bleeding is associated with feelings of cruelty, suffering or punishment. Later each period becomes associated with this complex conflict situation and is accompanied by irritability and depression. If the guilt feelings are paramount, the first period may cause the onset of an acute psychosis or neurosis. Another possibility is a disturbance of physiological functioning such as amenorrhea, dysmenorrhea, or excessive bleeding.

With the onset of menstruation, the girl is also faced with the assumption of reproductive feminine functioning, i.e., pregnancy and childbirth, which may appear more as a hope or a fear. There is a deep unconscious association between fantasies of birth and death. Thus, in the girl's unconscious, each menstruation may represent the disappointment in the expectation of a child.

Premenstrual depressions may also be connected with this disappointment. They seem to be related to an inner perception of the biologic experience of postovulatory changes in the menstrual cycle.

Therese Benedek (1952) found that certain fluctuations and changes of psychosexual functioning in female analysands coincided with different phases of the menstrual cycle as determined by examination of daily vaginal smears and temperature recordings during analysis.

Bower and Altschule (1956) describe specific changes in pituitary-ovarian and pituitary-adrenal functioning in a group of patients suffering from postpartum psychosis.

Menzer (1953) considers interrelationships of pituitary-ovarian and psychological factors in dysmenorrhea.

Menzer-Benaron and Sturgis (1957), using concurrent psychoanalytic with endocrinological research methods in patients with dysmenorrhea, amenorrhea, and premenstrual tension, established strong evidence for the finding that specific emotional conflicts in menstrual and reproductive disorders of women are associated with specific disturbed endocrine functioning. They state that (a) conflicts primarily concerning sexual and reproductive functioning have their physiological counterpart in disturbances of the pituitary-ovarian axis. (b) More general conflicts not directly concerned with sexuality, such as aggression, depression, and ego boundaries, have their physiological counterpart in disturbances of the pituitary-adrenal functioning.

Fox et al. (1958), describing daily observations of urinary steroids and urinary pepsins during a three-year analysis of a male patient, state that the results support certain tentative hypothesis concerning correlations of disturbances in relatively constant biochemical and physiological balances with psychological defense equilibria. The feasibility of intensive psychological and endocrine correlative research was further demonstrated by Fox (1953, 1958) and Fox et al. (1957), who established that the rise or fall of urinary hydrocorticoids was associated with increases or decreases in adrenocortical function in response to certain acute psychological conflict situations.

METHODS OF THIS STUDY

Patients selected for this study have a complete physical and gynecological examination to exclude organic pathology of the reproductive system or other organic disorders. Preliminary endocrine assays include FSH, LH, and pregnanediol determinations of the urine to establish the status of the pituitary-ovarian axis, and several oxycorticoids and 17-ketosteroid determinations in 24-hour urine specimens to establish a baseline of adrenocorticoid functioning. The patients have one to two psychiatric interviews which furnish a history and establish a working diagnosis of the psychiatric disorder. Patients with overt psychosis or mental deficiency are excluded. In addition, there is a battery of psychological tests including TAT, Rorschach, and Draw-a-Person tests. Patients selected for intensive study are investigated concurrently from the psychological and endocrine point of view. Psychoanalysis or psychoanalytically oriented psychotherapy are used as a research method for psychologic observation as well as for therapeutic purposes. The continuously changing internal and external conflict situations allow the patients to be used as their own controls. With the development of the transference neurosis an opportunity is afforded to study the patients in various phases of developing and undoing the conversion processes.

Patients are initially informed of the nature of the research project and are offered analysis or therapy for a markedly reduced fee for their voluntary cooperation. They are asked by the gynecologist to keep a detailed menstrual calendar, marking date and duration of each period and presence of premenstrual symptoms or dysmenorrhea. It also includes evidence and date of ovulation if discernible to the patient. In addition, patients are requested to bring in weekly or bi-weekly 24-hour urine collections for determinations of pregnanediol, hydroxycorticoids, and 17-ketosteroid values. FSH and LH determinations are done as requested by the endocrinologist.

We are fully aware of the difficulties and conflicts that this research program per se arouses in the patient and the complications it produces in the transference neurosis. However, this aspect of the investigation will not be entered into in this presentation. Fox (1958) has discussed it thoroughly in his paper "Effect of Psychophysiological Research on the Transference."

CASE MATERIAL

The case to be presented is that of a young woman suffering from amenorrhea and asthma. In certain phases of her analysis this patient developed painless anovulatory bleeding, at other times she had pain-free ovulatory cycles or ovulatory cycles accompanied by dysmenorrhea and preceded by premenstrual tension. Intervals of amenorrhea persisted throughout the period of observation. Concurrent endocrine studies included bi-weekly pregnanediol, as well as 17-ketosteroid and hydroxycorticoid determinations on 24-hour urine specimens, as well as occasional FSH and LH determinations.

The case history (reconstructed in her analysis) as well as the course of her analysis provide illustrations of the development and undoing of the conversion process.

Alice, a twenty-five-year-old instructor in a university, consulted me because of amenorrhea following her first period at the age of eighteen; asthma of varying severity since the age of fourteen, and a work disturbance of about one year's duration. It also developed that she had several phobias, paramount among them a fear of doctors, explosions, and thunderstorms. She had consulted a local gynecologist because of his reputation as being interested in "emotional factors." She was diagnosed by him as a "functional hypothalamic estrogen deficiency amenorrhea," and referred for psychoanalysis.

She was born the oldest of four siblings in a Southern town where both her parents were college teachers. Her next eldest brother, her favorite, was born when she was about two years old; he suffered from asthma since early childhood, and during her adolescence became her only confidant (Hansel and Gretel). Her second brother was born when she was about three and a half years old. He was academically the most successful among the siblings, and envied by the patient. At the time of her first brother's birth, her father had an "acute nervous breakdown" which developed later into a chronic incapacitating neurotic illness. He had periods of withdrawal, when he would lock himself in a room, sometimes for several days. Occasionally he had violent rages, attacking and beating any of the children for mild misdemeanors if the mother was not around to protect them. When not in such a mood, he was mild and kind, but passive.

In addition to his "moods," her father suffered from severe hay fever and a chronic diarrhea. The patient remembers having been frightened by the noise of his nose-blowing, his violent sneezes, as well as the noise of his bowel movements which she could hear through the bathroom door.

Religion was taken very seriously by the family. Her father was demanding and intolerant in this area. Her mother subscribed to religion with even greater fervor, but was more tolerant. She was the spiritual leader of the home, more popular, active, and outgoing than her father, and also more successful in her work which she carried on in addition to the major duties of the household. She was a woman of great principle, "always involved in some great cause." At first the patient described her as a saint. Later, with bitterness, she said, "Mother used goodness as a weapon against all of us." The mother was often worried and unhappy, complaining of the drudgeries imposed on her by her husband and children. She accused herself of being a bad mother if her children behaved badly or seemed troubled. She had a mild heart condition and arthritis, but disregarded discomfort, saying she had no time to indulge in sickness, and tried to instill the same principles in her children. She gave them little affection because "it was bad to spoil them," but was greatly concerned with their moral growth. She was strict but fair, and from an early age insisted they control their emotions, especially aggression, by reason. Until the patient was nine years old she was the only girl in the family and considered herself her father's favorite, loving him in spite of the fear of his rage, and her hurt feelings over his frequent withdrawal.

When Alice was a little over eight, her mother informed her she was pregnant, and that the new sibling would arrive as her birthday present. She was elated by this news, and felt cheated when the baby arrived two weeks after her birthday. She felt that now she had lost both her mother and the baby. As this sister grew older, Alice resented her more and more, since she felt that she was taking away her own position as father's favorite. She relates most of her childhood unhappiness to the birth of this sister.

When the children complained to their mother about their father's remoteness or moods, she would defend him, although later she made it clear to her daughter that she despised him for his weakness and regretted being trapped in the marriage. Although the patient herself felt that her father was weak, she attributed this to his having been emasculated by her mother's competition and her "goodness," but she never dared openly to take his side. She only remembers a single occasion in her childhood when she was the victim of her father's rage. She was very frightened by the cruel beating she received and humiliated by the fact that she afterwards urinated on the floor.

The patient recalled with bitterness that her mother sent her to nursery school shortly after her brother was born, when she was only two years old. Later in school she did well and learned with enthusiasm which earned her the praise of both parents. However, she always felt lonely and had few friends. Her time at home was spent in helping her mother with household duties which she resented. She also was an "assistant mother" looking after her three younger siblings. She enjoyed being their confidante, feeling they were closer to her than to mother. She would intercede for them when mother felt disciplinary measures were called for, and would help them in concealing things from both parents. This protectiveness would break down whenever she felt that one of them, especially the boys, was getting preferential treatment. She was envious of her brothers for being boys and always felt that her mother preferred them for this reason. She dates this back to about age three when she became aware of the difference in sexes while watching her brother urinate. Made very envious of the male genital, she consoled herself with the fantasy that she had a little penis inside which would grow into a big one like her brother's later on. She acted out this fantasy by urinating into bottles or containers, while in an upright position. She also withheld her urine as long as she possibly could and then enjoyed the resulting forceful stream and large quantity of urine which gave her a feeling of masculinity and power. This behavior persisted into late adolescence and was one of the patient's most jealously guarded secrets. Her behavior pattern in regard to moving her bowels is also of interest. Her mother insisted on regularity and would give her an enema if she failed to produce a daily bowel movement. She was often constipated and reacted to the enemas with mixed feelings of humiliation and pleasure. When she was about ten years old, she began to keep her constipation a secret from her mother to avoid enemas. However, when the constipation persisted for more than a week, she would "confess" because then the enjoyment of the enemas outweighed the negative feelings because the evacuation was so big.

At the age of ten Alice had a tonsillectomy, one of the most traumatic experiences of her youth. She remembered that her mother was present during the operation, holding her down while she was being strapped to the operating table. She felt that her mother had been of no help during her terror of being smothered by the anesthesia. Following the operation she developed a chronic nasal discharge which she perceived as dirty and disgusting like her father's hay fever. She dates the onset of most of her phobias to this time of life. There also developed a subtle change in her relationship to her mother whom she began to distrust. This expressed itself in periods of withdrawal and moroseness similar to her father's. Intellectual achievement became increasingly important. She did very well at school, but could never enjoy it since she was intensely competitive and could not tolerate the success of others.

At the age of fourteen, Alice had the first attack of asthma.

This was triggered by an incident in which her father accused her of having stolen his favorite knife. Hurt and angry she ran to her mother who comforted her by saying, "You know how crazy father is." She felt that father's accusation had been justified on a symbolic level since she had "stolen" his position in the family. Following this incident the patient had frequent asthma attacks. She also began to rebel openly against her father which led to many angry altercations between them. This rebellion was supported by her mother who rationalized it by saying, "Every healthy person has to go through a stage of rebellion to grow up."

When Alice was fourteen years old, her mother had a hysterectomy for a benign uterine growth. By this time she had begun to develop the bodily changes associated with the menarche but failed to menstruate. She felt embarrassed by looking female, whereas the failure of menstruation increased her hope of eventually getting a penis. When she was eighteen, she suffered from a mysterious illness consisting of lethargy, fever, and anorexia, associated with a state of reverie, which she experienced as pleasant. After two months, a homeopath was consulted who diagnosed the illness as "repressed menstruation." He decided to give her a pill to bring on menstruation. The patient first refused, but was threatened with hospitalization and injections. In a helpless rage, she took the pill and menstruated the following day. She had a violent temper tantrum in which she struck her mother who remained calm and tried to console her by saying, "You should be glad to menstruate, it means you can have babies." This statement made the patient more angry since it meant she would have to wait so long. The period only lasted one day and was associated with violent cramps. Alice attributed this short duration to "shock and fury" and was pleased when no further periods occurred. Her ability to suppress the hated femininity gave her a feeling of secret power. She kept the amenorrhea a secret from her mother, as she had previously concealed her constipation.

There was one exception in her estrangement from mother, i.e., when the two of them would go mountain climbing together. The memories of these outings belong to the patient's most cherished ones. "There was a deep feeling of belonging together, of almost being one." They enjoyed the physical effort of climbing and the feeling of being on top of the world. The patient reports that when they would start on these outings while she had asthma, the asthma would disappear.

At the age of eighteen she went to a liberal women's college where she felt liberated from the shackles of her family. During the first year, she was relatively happy, making friends for the first time in her life. Conflicts arose when she became intensely jealous of some of her friends who did not confine their relationship to her. Again she turned to her studies in a competitive way and found herself frustrated by the better performance of other students.

In her unhappiness she consulted the school psychiatrist whom she saw in psychotherapy for about three months. She developed an intensely dependent relationship to him, which greatly frightened her. Soon she began to miss appointments and treatment was discontinued with his recommendation for her to be analyzed. During this psychotherapy, the patient began to menstruate for the second time, but menstruation ceased as soon as treatment was discontinued.

Shortly afterwards she fell in love with a young law student who was intelligent, intensely moral, asthmatic, and strongly tied to his mother (fusion of both her brothers). When she became aware of sexual feelings toward him accompanied by an intense jealousy of all his other friends, she became frightened and provoked him to break off the relationship. When he did, she reacted with depression and asthma. After termination of this first romance, she threw herself into her studies and graduated successfully.

After receiving her degree, she decided—because of a feeling of intellectual inferiority—not to continue her studies. She obtained the position which after three years she was still holding at the time she came for treatment. After doing brilliantly for a year, her work deteriorated because of competitive relationships with her contemporaries and a dependent, hostile attachment to one of her male superiors.

During the year preceding her decision to seek help, there had been two important events in her personal life. (1) Her favorite brother had married and his wife was expecting a baby. (2) She had become involved in a second love affair, this time with a brilliant, but extremely dependent, passive man whom she wanted to marry. Her mother advised against it: "He is like your father and will trap you into an unhappy marriage like mine." The patient submitted, as usual, to her mother. During this love affair, the patient had two menstrual periods with dysmenorrhea, but menstruation ceased after the affair was broken off. What decided her to seek treatment was a feeling she had miserably failed in the area of intellectual achievement, her personal relationships, and in her abortive attempt to be a woman.

After one and a half years of preparatory psychotherapy, analysis was started, which is still in progress after three years. During the first months of analysis, the patient went through a stage of testing out the analyst by hostile and provocative behavior. This was followed by about a week of severe attacks of asthma for which she blamed the shift from therapy to analysis, since she felt that she had lost the analyst as a person. She feared that the position on the couch would deprive her of her own individuality and make her into a puppet. Then she confessed that she had been afraid of sexual feelings toward the analyst as well as of her liking the dependent position. She menstruated during the first month of her analysis. Her reaction to this was: "It's my female self that is starting out. That is your fault."

After a temporary recurrence of the hostile behavior which followed the summer vacation during which menstruation ceased, she settled down into a regressive, oral-passive transference relationship, which lasted about six months. This was characterized by a feeling of loss of identity not accompanied by anxiety. In the transference situation the analyst's identity kept switching from female to male, while in her fantasies and dreams she saw herself as a dependent baby or body-phallus. She endowed the analyst with magical powers and the possession of an attachable and detachable "slug" (a worm-like creature of changeable size), in which these powers were contained. As long as she passively united with the analyst, all would be well.

During this time, she did her work in a perfunctory fashion and spent a great deal of her time in reveries about the past and the relation to the analyst. Accompanying this material there was an under-current in which she saw herself as a "phoney" and her peaceful state as an illusion which could not last. The "mystical union" would be interrupted only by cancelled interviews. In response, she would become either enraged, depressed, or asthmatic.

In spite of this marked psychological regression, she had six ovulatory periods without discomfort at fairly regular intervals. Her adrenal hormone excretion seemed normal without undue fluctuations.

When she found out on one occasion that the analysis was to be interrupted for two weeks, she reacted with panic, nightmares, and a semidelusional episode during the last analytic hour in which she felt herself actually attacked by the slug. On this one occasion her hydrocorticoid excretion reached highly abnormal levels. During the vacation she was shocked by the intensity of her murderous rage and the fantasies accompanying it. She had temper tantrums, taking out her anger on whoever was available. This was followed by harsh self-accusations.

After analysis was resumed, the relationship changed from a passive to an aggressive oral one, with fantasies of being devoured by the analyst represented as a witch, or a demon, and of her devouring the analyst from inside. The "slug" was still present, ready to attack her, and was occasionally perceived as her attacking self. During this time, her first boy friend reappeared on the scene. She resumed relations with him, quite consciously to protect herself from the intensive transference feelings. She had one episode of anovulatory spotting, which she simultaneously viewed as castration and abortion, and then became amenorrheic for three months.

During this time she became dissatisfied with her job and started to look for one which was intellectually more challenging. After her boy friend left, she became amenorrheic and began to view herself as predominantly male. She became increasingly competitive and aggressive. Some of her aggressive impulses were acted out by surreptitiously attacking some of her female co-workers and some of my analysands, making it appear accidental. Such episodes would be followed by intense retaliatory fear, the need to provoke punishment, and later by self-accusatory recrimination and asthma. She saw herself as a monster with a big mouth and attacking teeth.

There was an increasing need for independence which she acted out in planning a hitchhiking and mountain-climbing trip through the Canadian Rockies. This was associated with ideas of revenge for desertion of her during analysis. During this time her adrenal hormone excretion started to show abnormally wide fluctuations. She carried out her planned vacation trip, but she had a miserable time, suffering from a feeling of intense loss and frequent attacks of asthma. She was also amenorrheic.

The next analytic year was the most stormy one. It was

characterized by a regression to an anal-sadistic level lasting
for about six months. During this time she was constantly
overwhelmed by violent sadistic fantasies. She performed
quite well in her work, but was plagued by competitive and
envious feelings. As later confessed, this state was associated
with masturbatory activity consisting of a drawing out of the
clitoris, accompanied by fantasies that it represented a penis
which she used for anal attack on mother, father, or the analyst. She fluctuated between acting out her aggression outside analysis and fits of self-accusatory depression, as well as
increasingly severe asthma. She was so afraid of her aggression
and homosexual feelings that she isolated herself socially.
During this time, she was either amenorrheic or had anovulatory spotting. This represented either castration or abortion
to her, for which the analyst, representing the phallic mother
or revengeful father, was held responsible. In either case, the
spotting seemed to represent a partial undoing of the conversion process. She reacted to the bleeding with violent anger.
In her analysis she was defiant and withholding, making it
clear that she was keeping her secrets. Occasionally she could
not tolerate the couch and had to sit up. She had nightmares
in which the analyst, in various disguises, would either
threaten her or attack her physically with guns or knives.
Then she would feel remorseful and attack herself for her
evil thoughts and behavior, becoming depressed to the point
of being suicidal with violent self-destructive fantasies. Masturbatory activity during the self-destructive stages would
consist of tearing at her clitoris, accompanied by fantasies of
being torn to pieces or crucified. During this phase of analysis, the urinary indices of adrenocortical activity fluctuated
more widely than ever before with an increase in abnormally
high and also of unusually low values. Finally she developed
asthma of great severity which lasted for several days and for
the first time consulted an internist. She cooperated in taking
her medication which led to a rapid improvement of the

asthma. This episode represented a reliving in transference of the mysterious pill incident to her, which led to her blaming the analyst and the internist for having stolen her internalized penis or baby by relieving her of her asthma.

Following this there occurred a turn to passivity with fantasies concerning anal sexual attacks performed on her by either her father or phallic mother. These were associated with great jealousy of her younger sister or her substitutes. At this time she was able to free herself from her social isolation, establish and re-establish friendships with women. In contrast to the previous phase at the beginning of the analysis, the turn toward femininity was not accompanied by giving up interest in her work. On the contrary, her efficiency increased but was more closely associated with a need to please her boss, whom she admired. The amount of her anovulatory bleeding increased considerably and was now associated with sexual fantasies during states of reverie. The bleeding now mainly represented loss of sphincter control and was associated with masochistic fantasies accompanied by feelings of internal sexual pleasure (father's beating). Guilt feelings were now related more definitely to aggressive feelings toward her mother as a rival. Asthmatic attacks were milder and of shorter duration. They occurred in connection with slights experienced in reality or the transference situation and could occasionally be stopped by the patient by resorting to fantasies of being raped. She then developed ovulatory periods preceded by severe premenstrual tension and accompanied by severe cramps. This ovulatory menstruation apparently represented a complete undoing of the amenorrhea conversion. It occurred as a result of fantasied sexual attack by father with resulting punishment (castration or abortion) by the envious mother. The feelings during the premenstrual phase represented her reaction to the imagined attack by the avenging mother accompanied by the same aggressive self-destructive fantasies and behavior characteristic of the anal-aggressive phase earlier in the analysis. Often the asthma or other conversion symptoms appeared as the only way she could deal with the aggressive self-destructive drives as well as the sexual tensions thus released. She also struggled unsuccessfully against masturbation stimulated by the appearance of definite vaginal sensations. The third year of analysis is still characterized by a predominance of passive anal material. The aggressive acting out, destructiveness, and asthma have in general markedly decreased. She has also been able to discuss her feelings and fantasies connected with masturbation. Her good work performance continues and a more definite undercurrent of oedipal material is appearing. This is accompanied by more regularly occurring ovulatory periods.

Detailed clinical observations of this patient with amenorrhea and asthma have illustrated the way in which the physiological disturbances reflected the unconscious attempt to make restitution for the early experience of losses—which were reflected in the development of the transference neurosis. These included the loss of mother's affection (breast) to her brothers and later to a younger sister, whom she also held responsible for a shift in her father's affection away from herself. When around the age of three she discovered the anatomical differences between the sexes, she reacted with intense penis envy as well as a fantasy that she herself had a small inside penis which later would develop into a big and adequate male organ. This fantasy was acted out by withholding her urine for long periods of time and urinating into a container in an upright position with a feeling of being powerful and masculine.

At fourteen, in the setting of her mother's hysterectomy and following a disturbing episode during which her father accused her of stealing his knife, she developed asthma, which has been interpreted as providing symbolic restitution for the lost father and the lost baby (her perception of the birth of her younger sister) on an oral and anal level. Although the patient had developed the secondary sex characteristics of menarche by the age of fourteen, she did not menstruate until the age of eighteen after she was forced by her mother to take a pill from a homeopath in order to induce menstrual bleeding. After this experience which the patient perceived as a castration, menstruation ceased again for seven years. It was then gradually re-established with various psychophysiological aberrations during the course of psychoanalysis.

DISCUSSION

From the analytic investigation of this case and others not reported here, certain tentative conclusions regarding the psychophysiological disturbances of the menstrual cycle can be reached. These disturbances—including amenorrhea, anovulatory bleeding, dysmenorrhea, and premenstrual tension —can be viewed as different stages of complicated conversion processes dealing with two major problems in different qualitative and quantitative distributions. One is an attempt at symbolic restitution of early losses of maternal and paternal partial objects; this attempt becomes associated and fused with primitive oral and anal impregnation fantasies. The other is the restitution of the genital trauma by symbolic retrojection of the phallus.

These early problems are usually reactivated during the menarche or in later adult life by actual or symbolic re-experience of the various losses and will then lead to a completion of the conversion process with various symptoms of menstrual dysfunction. This conversion process is usually set in motion in young girls who suffer severe and actual losses involving different aspects of both parental figures. These losses usually take place during the pregenital stage before the height of the oedipus complex is reached. An attempt is made to deal with these losses through symbolic retrojection of the ambivalently loved partial parental objects (breast, anal and phallic penis). This in turn leads to a marked intensification of the sense of castration and penis envy and is accompanied by an increase in aggressive impulses. An attempt is then made to solve the genital trauma by retrojection of "father's" or "mother's" phallus. Thereupon emerges the conscious fantasy of possessing a male organ, either in the form of a "hidden inside penis" or as represented by the hope of further growth of the clitoris into an adequate male organ. During the time of the oedipus complex—after the retrojection of the phallus—most of these girls act out their masculine fantasies either by clitoral masturbation and/or by peculiar behavior involving urination. This consists of urinating in the erect position, or of withholding urine for long periods of time with the idea of producing a large and powerful masculine stream referred to as a "waterfall" or "pool." This behavior is interpreted as actual proof of possessing the desired male organ and is accompanied by feelings of pride and power. It often persists into latency and early adolescence. It is usually associated with a highly ambitious and competitive turn to masculine achievement mainly in intellectual and athletic spheres of accomplishment. For instance, one amenorrheic patient consciously identified herself with Joan of Arc whom she perceived as the greatest military and spiritual leader of France, surpassing all men in physical prowess and intellectual ability. The simultaneous identification with Joan of Arc as the saint and martyr was consciously denied and could only be demonstrated after prolonged analysis. It is historically documented in the transcript of Joan of Arc's trial that her conscious denial of femininity was also associated with amenorrhea.

The great need to surpass all men goes hand in hand with intense penis envy and castrating behavior. This in turn leads to intense guilt feelings and usually produces inhibitions of creative ability.

The turn to masculine activity is usually accompanied by conscious denial and devaluation of femininity. However, on a deeper and often unconscious level primitive oral and anal passive sexual fantasies can usually be demonstrated. Fantasies of oral and anal impregnations become fused with the previously described maternal and paternal retrojects and assume a highly threatening quality. Being located "inside the abdomen," they may lead to eating difficulties, i.e., anorexia or bulimia; or disturbances of bowel and bladder function such as constipation, diarrhea, or enuresis. The two last named are associated with feelings of guilt and shame since they indicate poor sphincter control and carry the fantasy meaning of a lack of control over sexual and aggressive impulses. They often become associated with feelings of guilt over masturbation. It is interesting to note that many patients have an intense need to keep the bowel and urinary disturbances secret—a behavior pattern which is later transferred to the menstrual disturbances.

During the psychophysiological upheaval of the menarche, the genital trauma is always reactivated. If, in adidtion, any of the early pregenital traumata are reactivated through actual or symbolic re-experience of the losses, menstrual dysfunction will usually replace the early bowel or bladder disturbances. This also may occur later in adult life through experiences which threaten bodily integrity (operations, accidents, or severe illnesses) and thus reactivate the genital trauma, or through actual or symbolic losses of parental figures or their surrogates. The nature, severity, and reversibility of these conversion symptoms will depend on the nature, severity, and timing of the initial and secondary losses, and on the psychological and physiological maturity of the individual patients at the time these losses occur. In general, it can be stated that if the losses involve primarily figures which are perceived as maternal and feminine by the patient, the symptoms tend to be anovulatory bleeding, dysmenorrhea, or premenstrual tension. If they involve primarily figures perceived as phallic or paternal, amenorrhea will usually be the result. If the primary losses occurred during the oral phase and were maintained by continued and severe deprivation, the eating disturbances along with the menstrual dysfunction usually persist and tend to become firmly entrenched and irreversible, i.e., anorexia nervosa. With the appearance of menstrual conversion symptoms the early bowel and urinary disturbances usually disappear. They tend to reappear temporarily when during the analysis of the transference neurosis the menstrual conversion process is undone.

Amenorrhea is the final symptom of a long and complicated conversion process. It is usually connected with fixation at or regression to the oral-aggressive or anal-sadistic stage of development. It represents retrojection of the paternal or maternal phallus in restitution for the early sense of genital trauma, and also serves to express primitive impregnation fantasies fused with early maternal and paternal introjects. It is regarded as a protection against intolerable sexual and aggressive drives.

Anovulatory bleeding occurs frequently in pubescent girls for several months before ovulatory menstruation is fully established. It may persist as a conversion symptom or may appear in amenorrheic patients when the conversion process is undone during analysis.

(1) In an oral- or anal-aggressive setting, it represents a revival of the castration-abortion trauma viewed as a retaliatory attack by a phallic parental figure. The bleeding mobilizes intense anxiety and strong aggressive impulses which are either directed against the threatening object or turned against the self.

(2) In an anal-passive setting, anovulatory bleeding occurs in relation to fantasied sexual attack. It then represents a loss of sphincter control which is accompanied by passive

masochistic fantasies and feelings of shame and guilt. It often coincides with the first conscious drive toward femininity.

Ovulatory menstruation—a complete undoing of the conversion process—may occur in the setting of a symbiotic mother-child transference experienced as restoring all that has been previously lost. This might help to explain the occurrence of physiologically "normal menstruation" in very infantile and dependent girls and women. Their menstruation occurs as if in symbiosis with a mother or mother surrogate and does not include an inner experience of femininity. Under these circumstances there is no premenstrual tension or menstrual discomforts. However, the maintenance of such a regular asymptomatic cycle depends entirely on the actual presence of this mother figure in the patient's surroundings. In cases of physical separation from the mother for whatever reasons, menstrual conversion symptoms will make their appearance.

In a more anal-passive setting of the transference, ovulatory menstruation was either preceded by premenstrual tension and/or accompanied by dysmenorrhea. It occurs as the result of a fantasied sexual attack followed by punishment by the rival parental figure. The bleeding then represented a loss of the fantasied baby in addition to a revival of the genital trauma. In this pattern there is a marked release of aggressive impulses during the premenstrual phase with acting out of projected hostility frequently leading to feelings of guilt and depression. The dysmenorrhea can be viewed as a new conversion symptom dealing predominantly with ideas of the lost mother and the lost child, and to a lesser extent with the lost penis. When ovulatory menstruation occurred in previously amenorrheic patients, it was often associated with the appearance of vaginal sensations in a previously anesthetic vagina. This often coincided with an increasing turn to feminine masochism, passivity, and narcissism.

The undoing of the conversion symptom in patients with

menstrual dysfunction is almost always heralded with a marked increase in anxiety in conjunction with the release of previously repressed aggressive and sexual impulses. Sometimes this anxiety is so severe that transitory psychotic episodes, mood disturbances, or psychopathic behavior patterns may occur. Other patients react with the appearance of new conversion symptoms in other parts of the body. When intolerable aggressive and sexual impulses were not sufficiently neutralized by the conversion process or were remobilized by the undoing of the conversion symptom in the process of analysis, this was physiologically correlated to an increased output and an abnormally wide fluctuation in the amounts of urinary substances reflecting adrenal cortical activities.

11.

SYMPTOM FORMATION AND MALE HOMOSEXUALITY

JEROME L. WEINBERGER, M.D.

This paper illustrates the concept of the conversion process developed by Felix Deutsch and elaborated clinically by the Workshop on the Theory of the Conversion Process. According to this concept, the conversion process is continually active. It aims at restoring the sense of loss of a part of the body by retrojection, and is maintained through the symbolic representation of the organ or body part. The process of loss, restitution through retrojection, and symbolization is illustrated in homosexuality. Male homosexuality is an attempt to be intact or whole. In symptom formation in male homosexuality, both the expression of the incompleteness and the loss of masculinity and its restitution are illustrated.

The resolution of anxiety arising from the instinctual demands results in the various compromise formations with which we are familiar in the psychoneuroses. The symptom formation that occurs is an expression of the defenses available to the ego, the intactness of the ego, and the strength of the instincts. Especially where the ego is weak in relationship to the instinctual drives, symptoms representing earlier modes of dealing with instinctual energy appear. The bodily expression, or the leap into the physical sphere as the conversion symptom, may represent genital or pregenital aspects of ego organization, ranging from conversion hysteria to hypochondriasis. They may also serve as an index of the relative intactness of the ego in dealing with its instinctual demands, the superego, and the environment.

Usually conversion symptoms are not the presenting reason for treatment in homosexuality. The homosexuality itself appears to be an expression of both the defense against aggressive and libidinal impulses and also their gratification. Homosexuality may be considered the total acting out of the symptom not only as an object relationship through the homosexual act, partial as that may be, but also as the total relationship of the homosexual to all aspects of his environment and to himself. In some cases conversion symptoms appear transiently as the bodily expression of the homosexuality. These symptoms reveal the essential meaning of the homosexual defense for the patient.

In *Three Essays on the Theory of Sexuality* (1905a), Freud described the manifestations of infantile sexuality and defined homosexuality as the persistence of these elements into adult life, and stated that neurosis (symptom formation) was the "negative (or the transformation) of the perversions." In later works by Freud, the concept of homosexuality as a defense became clearer, as in the defenses related to the oedipus complex in "A Child is Being Beaten" (1919). With the advent of ego psychology (Freud, 1923c), concepts concerning early ego development have been studied in the etiology of homosexuality. Greenacre (1952) has stressed that the orderly development may be disturbed by overstimulation or premature libidinization of the infant. She suggests that the overstimulation is traumatic to the infant in the first years of life and serves to intensify the infant's primary identification. With increased narcissism, the infant's sense of reality is impaired because of augmented responsiveness of the body. She adds that this heightened responsiveness may be a factor in the belief in magic, since the somatic aspects in the identification give it the semblance of reality. Premature libidinization leads to seeking gratification through need-satisfying objects rather than identification. Without identification there is defective development of the ego and superego (Johnson, 1949).

Acting out is considered a substitute for remembering (Freud, 1914c). It represents an earlier phase of development in which direct motor discharge has not yet been postponed in the service of reality testing in the management of anxiety. It reflects aspects of the primary process that persist, owing to some faults in identification. Children react with behavior rather than words, which is an expression of the primary process. Internalization, symbol formation and intellectualization are aspects of the ego development as a result of successful identification; these consist of the ascendancy of the secondary process in dealing with reality (Kanzer, 1957).

Defects in ego development appear in areas of reality which are acted out. In terms of bodily symptoms, the ego fragments or deficiencies appear in transient, destructive symptoms in which the body is being injured or destroyed. The ego defect as it appears in the conversion symptom reflects the deficiency in the binding of the aggressive instinct. Homosexuality may be viewed as acting out, as a defense utilized by the ego to deal with anxiety in a direct way.

Discussing the various clinical entities of homosexuality, Nacht et al. (1956) state, "that it is difficult to define in a single formula the ego defences of homosexuals. The career of the homosexual in no way protects him against all the dangers of neurotic and psychotic vicissitudes, the homosexual position being able to be considered only one of the defence methods against the unconscious fear of being broken up."

That narcissism is the defense of the weak ego (Freud, 1914b) is seen in children (Bernstein, 1957), and as a restitutive process in psychosis (Gates and Weinberger, 1955). Bychowski (1945) states that the homosexual activity is an effort to overcome the narcissism and to restore object relations, and that homosexuality wards off depression and depersonalization.

It is of major significance that the homosexual patient does not come for treatment because of bodily symptoms. It is well known that symptoms serve as the (ego expression) compromise formation for the id and the superego. The symptom or the cathexis of the body may be for some a hold on reality. In conversion hysteria, a stable relation to reality and to objects is maintained through symptoms. However, where pregenital elements appear, with poorly bound aggressive and libidinal impulses, together with part and labile object relationships, bodily symptoms will have the intensity derived from the earliest developmental phases, namely, the anal and the oral. It may be due to this intensity, which magnifies the castration fears of the homosexual, that acting out appears as a massive defense. Symptom formation in homosexuals is seen more frequently than one would suspect from the literature. One may suggest that the homosexual act in its narcissistic and concrete nature serves as a restitutive process which gratifies the latent wish for completeness, omnipotence and power. The homosexual feels weak and defective. The need to restore and secure himself against the fears of the outside world (projection), an expression of aggressiveness against outside objects who represent early objects and the fear of retaliation, is expressed in the total life situation of the homosexual.

Glauber (1956) views the restitutive wish of the homosexual fantasy and act as an unconscious rebirth—a transformation from the castrated, passive, destructive identification with the mother while retaining her active phallic aspects. He stresses that incomplete identifications result in an unstable ego, consisting of passive incorporative aims and destructive cathexis of the part self-images and part objects which are mutually destructive. The homosexual perversion is both an aborted identification and an acting out. No psychic change or real integration takes place, merely a temporary reduction of psychic tension by externalization or projection of one or several of its ego fragments which are not miscible with the rest. This compromise follows essentially the process of symptom formation as seen in the transference neuroses and is in accord with the principle of the repetition compulsion, derivative of the aggressive drive.

The conversion symptoms in the homosexual manifest themselves as a more direct expression of castration fears, intensified by oral-sadistic and sadomasochistic elements of early development. This intensification of bodily symptoms does not serve as well in allaying anxiety as the acting out process constituting the homosexuality. The perversion appears to be the negative of the neurosis (or symptom formation) on a pregenital level, serving as a defense against the bodily expression of castration anxiety (Ferenczi, 1914). It would appear that Freud's dictum—the neurosis is the negative of the perversion—is dependent on the presence of an intact ego and superego, where secondary-process thinking is dominant and has replaced the impulsivity and the acting out of primary-process characteristics of the defective ego.

The following two patients illustrate the occurrence and alternation of conversion symptoms with overt homosexuality. In the first patient, the symptom formation can be seen as a beginning process which never developed fully. In the second case, symptom formation was fully developed and alternated with periods of homosexuality.

CASE MATERIAL

D. M., a tall, slender, twenty-three-year old engineer, was in analysis for three years and eight months. His initial complaints were his fear of continuing life as a homosexual, his uncertainty and unsureness. He felt his penis was defective because it was bent the wrong way when erect. In addition, he believed he was sterile. Since childhood he had had hay fever, which served to keep him from military service. Once during the month of August he sneezed during the hour and recalled splashing in a pool as a baby. The hay fever during the time of the analysis was so mild that outside of the analysis no symptoms were recognized.

The patient dated his homosexuality to the age of fourteen, when he indulged in mutual masturbation with another boy. Although he dated girls in his teens, his mutual masturbation continued until his friend became interested in girls. During the next four years, at a private boarding school for boys, he began dating one girl steadily. During this time he pursued with zeal his interest in radio and electronics and motors. He built high-fi sets for himself and for the faculty. In college he pursued his interest in electrical engineering.

In his third year, his grades were so poor that he was dropped from college. This event mobilized him to the extent that he obtained a position with an atomic energy research group. In this area he could drive his car as fast as he liked. He also learned to fly a plane. The interest in powerful motors and flying had begun very early in his teens, first as an interest in motorized equipment of every sort, and was later pursued in his profession. He returned to college after his year of work and completed his senior year, graduating as an electronics engineer.

Shortly after his graduation, his father died. Immediately thereafter he became an active homosexual. His chief homosexual interest was seeing the other person's penis and indulging in mutual masturbation. On two occasions during the analysis he did "everything," referring to fellatio and sodomy, which was repugnant to him. Compulsively he would seek out boys in parks, always fearful of being caught, black-mailed or injured by them.

The patient worked as an electronics engineer in a univer-sity-affiliated research group. Here he kept aloof from his co-workers. He was continually late for work and provoked his superiors by numerous irritating acts. He would stuff ciga-rette butts into coke bottles until they were full, dump his ash tray on the floor, appear late from lunch eating a choco-late ice cream cone which he managed to drip on his superi-or's shoes.

He spent every week end at a camp where a group of boys and men were engaged in repairing engines of cars and loco-motives. During the week he occasionally saw a girl at the radio station, where he had spent a great deal of time. He endured the week to get to the week end, when he and his colleagues indulged in heavy manual labor, wore work clothes, became greasy and dirty and lived in primitive bar-racks.

The patient is an only child. Of the greatest significance was his father's handicap—an artificial left lower limb. Mr. D. M. Senior, while motorcycling in Europe at the age of twenty, was in an accident which resulted in the amputation of his left lower leg. He limped on the left, was not able to run or be active with his son. He was very careful not to be seen unclothed by his son, so that the patient did not appear to know about his father's handicap. At the age of eight, he reported, his nurse told him that his father had a wooden leg. Mr. D. M. Senior was a meticulous man who was very methodical about financial matters. He had married at the age of thirty-six a woman about ten years his junior. Because of his age and his handicap, our patient felt his father was not like other fathers. He had to rest in the afternoon, and frequently the stump of his thigh would become irritated and bleed. Shortly after the patient's college graduation, his father developed a thrombophlebitis in his remaining right

leg. Gangrene occurred, so that an amputation was necessary. He also developed a cerebral hemorrhage and died of a
terminal pneumonia at fifty-eight.

The patient's mother had little to do with the care of her
son, who was turned over to nurses and the cook. The nurses
changed, but the cook was the constant figure who cared for
him. Until the age of nine he was rigidly bowel trained. He
was seated on the toilet until he defecated or was given an
enema. His ideas of the female genitals as dirty organs were
derived from his peeking at the various nurses in the bathroom. His mother, during his early years, was a distant figure
who kissed him good night before going out for the evening.
Growing up near a park, he was isolated from other children.
He envied the rough kids who came in gangs from the tough
section and wished to be free like them. He felt that his
father in his early years must have been a tough kid. But
mother made him into a neat little Lord Fauntleroy.

Throughout the analysis, his identification with his father
revealed itself in acting out in such ways as smashing his
hand and later his finger. In the first week of the analysis,
his nose was broken by two sailors he picked up. In this
regard, it is significant that he took a motorcycle trip, like
his father, in Europe when he was eighteen and had a near
accident. On a number of occasions he would come into the
office limping on the right side (his father limped on the left).
He related, "Father first lost the left leg, then the right. The
blood clotted. They gave him an anticlotting medicine. The
first day they got him up, he had a stroke." At this point the
patient had a picture of a light with black around it and
recalled the operation on his broken nose. His right leg was
in the air crossed over his left leg. He wondered about the
blood draining from it. It felt numb. He talked of how cruel
nature is: "When you get cold, there is less blood in the feet.
You get colder still. You can lose an ear, hands, limbs, then
the penis. What are you good for?"

The patient brought many dreams referring to damaged vital parts. These dreams dealt with engines and cars. For example, "I am looking up the exhaust pipe of a car and see the burned-out hot exhaust bearings." In association to this dream he related that his penis was defective. It was bent the wrong way. He wondered if his father had the same trouble with his penis. Father had a wooden leg, and he feared seeing his father urinating. He recalled that at the age of eight his nursemaid told him that his father had a limp. He had responded by saying that he did not see it. In a slip of speech he said, "She said I had a wooden leg—I mean he." The theme of the missing limb was repeated again and again in dreams. "I am talking with Henry B. about the engine. It is on its side without its housing or exhaust. He says it needs an exhaust. I say it works without one. It only gives off heat waves." His fears of being killed and castrated repeated themselves in fantasies of his hand being ripped off in a commutator and the thought of his penis being torn off. He had a fear of cancer. A mole on his left elbow which had been removed surgically two years before recurred. He thought of his father's leg amputation, that his arm would get no blood. The surgeon who operated on him had amputated his father's leg. He feared the carpenters at his place of work. He had a fantasy of a safe world, a United Nations where everyone would come naked so that everyone's penis could be seen.

The patient had two pictures of women—the fragile, pure, distant mother, and the messy, dirty nursemaids. The female genital was pictured as a cloaca—a dirty hole. He associated seeing nursemaids on the toilet. He recalled the smell of urine and feces in the Statue of Liberty during his visit there in childhood. During the latter part of his analysis while petting with a girl, he raised his arm in the attitude of the Statue of Liberty as a joke. The gesture, however, signified his feelings about the dirty female genital. Menstruation was

regarded as dirty. Mother was pictured as insisting on cleanliness and good manners. The rebellion against his bowel
training by the maids and his being made a sissy by mother
was manifested in his being slovenly in his clothes and keeping his room in a mess. A recurrent theme was that women
would injure him or castrate him by giving him a venereal
disease or that pins or needles would be present in the vagina
to injure him.

The patient dreamed, "I have a terminal board (electrical
equipment) in my mouth. I am pulling out bobbin pins of
two sizes." He associated the dream to mother's darning
needles, to the nurse holding pins in her mouth and the injection given him by a nurse when he had a nodule on his
penis. He was stuck by a pin when hugged by his maid.

The fear of castration for destructive and aggressive sexual
wishes toward women was a major theme. He recalled a
childhood friend who without training took off in his father's
airplane and got killed. The fear of being destroyed recurred
in dreams, as being cornered in a building by a car coming
in or by an atom bomb. The following dream illustrates his
anxiety over aggressive sexual wishes toward women as well
as his ego defenses. "In New York in a classroom where they
show that atom bombs dropped on buildings destroy the
center and the outside but not in between." He associated
New York with his mother and his anxiety about being questioned by a father of his friend. The classroom was associated
to his bed. It was quite clear that his need to be in between
or off center was his way to escape the destruction which he
feared from the outside world.

His sexual aggression toward women was related to his
confusion about anatomy and his ideas of sexual intercourse
as an assault with mutilation of the woman. His sexual exploration led to the discovery that the woman was not a
castrated man, the vagina was not where the penis would be.
The dream material illustrated his fantasy of the penis as a

weapon. This fantasy was also acted out in his identification with his piloting an airplane and being identified with fast-moving vehicles and large engines. He dreamed, "I am flying a B-29. I shut off the motors as I crash land, crunch into a slum building. There is an old woman inside. There is danger of three fires and setting gasoline aflame." In another dream, "I am in a boat with mother. A high-pitched sound comes from a jet motor. I tell mother to cover her ears. The sound mounts. Then the afterburner goes on. Mother did not cover her ears, and she writhes on the floor of the boat. She then covers them. Then I am in the concrete room where the jet motor controls are." He associated reading the story of a rape.

After having sexual intercourse for the first time, he dreamed, "Alice is driving my car. She is going fast. A police car shoots out. She goes right through it, leaving a neat hole. The cop is on the ground. His car is completely intact. Alice helps the cop. Everything is all right." In association to the dream he made a slip, saying in relation to Alice driving "Don't hit her"—referring to the police car. Although in the past he had associated his father with the policeman, women had been his policemen. It would appear that his car or penis referred to his feminine identification.

Ego defenses against his identification with a defective father led to acting out of his desperate search for a penis. His homosexuality was essentially a search for his father before amputation.

The patient's frantic search for a penis was represented in his work, creating new designs, working on motors and in piloting a plane. His whole body would become a penis of a gigantic order. In analysis he had feelings that his body was becoming gigantic in size, twice normal, as though it were hard to get through the door. He expressed his frustrated wish for a perfect and huge penis in the following dream, "We grow a needle-shaped crystal, a sapphire. I draw it out in a furnace. It is blue, clear and large, but the point shrinks and breaks. I say it will not work this way. It is priceless." In all these dreams he expresses feelings of defectiveness like his father and his search for the penis in life. He told the father of a friend that he was in analysis, and the comment was made that the school psychiatrist gave pills which some-times worked. The unconscious fantasy of being impregnated occurred with the thought of taking a pill. He spontaneously associated being blown up and the vision of a giant hand reaching for his penis and destroying it. These fears of cas-tration and the pregnancy fantasies referred to his analysis, being castrated and made into a woman.

Symptom formation in this patient is seen in an arrested and transient form. It consisted of an identification with his defective father. The conversion symptoms—the transient coldness and numbness of his limbs, limping, the illusion that his penis was bent and the feeling he was sterile—were of such a mutilating and destructive nature that symptom formation did not go further. Acting out had replaced symp-tom formation. The acting out expressed his difficulty in identification with both his mother and father in early life. His turning to machines as need-satisfying objects and as objects of identification was restitution for his fantasy of being defective and castrated. The engines, the airplanes, his vocation and his body itself all served as transient substitutes for his missing phallus. His homosexuality, a restitutive symp-tom, was acted out on account of his defective body image. His conversion symptoms were the direct expression of the defect in identification, ego formation, and his body image. The perversion can be said to be the negative of the symptom or the neurosis on a pregenital level. His relations to people were marked by negativism and hostility, derivatives from oral and anal levels, together with overwhelming fears of retaliation for his projected aggressive wishes. His transient hay fever during the analysis with reference to water and babies, together with the pregnancy fantasy expressed in taking a pill, revealed his identification with women. Anxiety-provoking as this was, this identification appeared to be more reassuring than the image of the injured father. Dynamically it would appear that his improvement was expressed in his last dream in which he identified himself with the woman who drove the car or had the penis. The penis referred to the father's missing penis that the women had taken. Its anal nature is seen in the material as the missing or burned-out exhaust pipes and as the afterburner of the jet plane. The homosexual act had served as protection against the fear of the loss of his defective penis. His bisexual wish was expressed by his search for a hairless, slim boy with a penis.

In the second case, symptom formation was fully established and alternated with active homosexuality.

N. E., a twenty-nine-year-old graduate student, was in analysis for a year and nine months. His initial symptoms consisted of fears of cancer of the genitals, fear of tuberculosis of the lung and Hodgkin's disease of the glands of the neck. He experienced feelings of fullness in his neck and throat and pains in the penis. He felt that his penis had become smaller. At various times during the analysis he complained of sores in his mouth, difficulty in swallowing and hoarseness due to a possible malignancy of the throat. After he stopped active homosexuality, he developed an itching in his axillae; he felt he had a recurrence of lice and at the same time he had a recurrence of hemorrhoids. Moreover, he regarded any minor ailment such as an upper respiratory infection as a major illness and was in a continual state of agitation concerning his physical condition for which he would see various doctors.

The patient became an active homosexual about the age of sixteen. As early as the age of ten or twelve he had had fantasies of loving masculine men. He had been in treatment for about a year with a therapist in another city before starting therapy with me. His homosexuality consisted of mutual masturbation and sodomy. Of considerable significance was the surgery he had for the eradication of a pilonidal cyst. He was operated on six times beginning at the age of nineteen.

The patient was a brilliant student, who graduated second in his college class and went on to do graduate work in English.

His mother was described as a domineering woman who never refused him anything, did all his errands and chores and became his source of support and reassurance in illness. He stated that mother regarded him as effeminate because he would not play ball with other boys and stayed with her all the time. His father was an immigrant who became moderately successful in business but who was passive in his home and was regarded by the patient with contempt. The patient's sister was four years older, married and had two children. The sister was very much attached to him and admired him tremendously. Analysis revealed that she was the princess of childhood, and he was the servant. The theme that she was the first child and first in her class at school recurred throughout the analysis. After hospitalization and cystoscopy for possible bleeding from the penis, he dreamed, "I am being examined by Dr. S. He finds a sinus in my penis. Just then a woman breaks in and says she wants to be seen first. She likes music and wants to hear Délibes, mentions pedantically Swan Lake." His mother and father visited him at the hospital. His mother took over situations, came first like in the dream. His father is small and old. The dream expressed the wish to be first like his sister and mother.

Indicative of the phallic primacy of the woman was the following dream, "I am with mother in a car with others. We have gotten a jewel. I am going in the water to protect it from others." He associated the jewel to his genital. He feared cancer of the palm of his right hand. He had great anxiety about his work and feared being mediocre. His mother called to help him with his car. His battery had gone dead.

This patient's identification with his mother and the fantasy of impregnation were exemplified in the dream, "I am having a wart removed from my neck. Mother has had it done. They put orange juice on it." He associated a man who drank three glasses of orange juice at a party and whose wife (a graduate student) was in her second pregnancy. His mother had a wart removed from her hand. The wound had gotten infected. He had a wart on his neck.

He regarded not only the image of himself as feminine, but also equated the breast with the penis, as in the following dream, "A male prostitute is in the bathroom. Joe and I pay $5 each. I go in first. He opens my fly but first makes a special movement, squeezing his nipple. It becomes a woman's breast. He sucks me. I go out and tell Joe." He associated that he had large nipples and wished to suck a man. In previous material, the gesture of touching his eye meant a breast was squeezed and milk got in it. The dream referred to his impotence which occurred with a prostitute.

During the course of the analysis, he became involved with a man whom he regarded as an ideal. The man was well built, hairless, the image of what he himself would have liked to be. With the onset of this homosexual affair, the patient's symptoms remitted. The analysis came to a standstill as his homosexuality flowered. When I suggested that he stop this relationship, his symptoms returned. He had itching in the axillae. He felt he had lice. His hemorrhoids recurred. After a period of abstinence, he would again relapse. During the abstinent periods he would be virtually panic-stricken with intense fears of various types of malignant illnesses such as cancer of the genitals, tuberculosis of the lungs and Hodgkin's disease of the glands of the neck. He would see various internists again and again and receive reassurance.

The following dream illustrated his anxiety toward women: "I am pursuing a sophomore. He turns into Anna (his girl friend) who gets into a car with her mother. I play with a squirrel to get Anna's attention and get her out of the car. Her mother puts her finger with a 'diamond' into the squirrel's mouth. I say it will be bitten off and she will lose the ring." It is quite clear that his anxiety was about losing his jewel in the squirrel's mouth or the female genital, but at the same time he identifies with the woman who has the diamond.

Another dream illustrates the patient's central problem. "I am Charles Francis Adams. I am going to adopt a child. The people who have the child are foreign. There are two young girls. I am to adopt one. The younger of the two is wearing an orange dress with lace going down the front, like a southern European costume. I say I decided not to adopt the girl. Then the younger one in the lace dress steps forward and dances. She appears very attractive. I reconsider. The dream stops at this point—undecided."

He stated that his mother was born in this country. Like Charles Francis Adams, she was positive and assertive. She wanted him to play with boys. "I am not muscular and well built like the all-American boy. I am built like a girl." The patient's sister teased and frightened him. She said he was adopted. "I would cry until my mother would reassure me." He stated that he exhibited himself to attract the masculine man, his homosexual ideal. The dream expressed his rivalry with his sister and his wish to be the first and the chosen one with his mother, the phallic woman.

He desperately sought to repair his defective image of himself. He was either anxiety-ridden, filled with ideas that he was desperately ill, or was well and homosexually active. In the anxious state he saw a continual parade of physicians, asking reassurance and treatment. However, he found his major reassurance in his mother. In panic he would telephone or fly home to her to be told, "It is all right. I had it too. Forget it."

His mother was the dominant figure in the family. She not only was the major figure in the life of the patient and his older sister but also with her two younger sisters. His mother served as an important aspect of his body image, as another aspect of being powerful and secure, as in the first dream of the woman with the diamond.

Using the image of his mother, he would seek out the "all-American boy" as his homosexual companion. This boy happened to have a disease of the lungs which was thought to be tuberculosis. The patient stayed with his companion while he was in the hospital, reassuring him with the exact words his own mother had said to him. He would then feel he had been contaminated with tuberculosis or some unknown disease of the lungs. He would become the defective sick boy and would ask his homosexual partner for reassurance. Then he would turn to various physicians and finally to his mother, becoming the dependent helpless child. Mother would then repeat her cliché, "It is all right. I have had the same symptoms too." Hodgkin's disease of the neck had been the disease from which the homosexual companion's brother died.

In his past the patient had had any blemish that appeared on his body, such as moles or unsightly hairs, removed surgically. When his acne of the back was so treated, it resulted in unsightly scarring. Because of this, he never appeared on the beach or on the tennis court without a covering shirt. He tried in all ways to be perfect in appearance. In his student days he had gone to extremes, including dangerous forms of cheating on exams, in order to be the perfect one as a student. However, he graduated second in his class and tried to give the impression of being first.

The need to have the perfect brain, to be the most desirable one socially and scholastically, can be seen as his attempt to counteract his feelings of defectiveness. He wished to be the opposite of his devaluated, unmasculine and shad-owy father. His interest in the arts and in intellectual pur-suits is seen in his dream wish to be an Adams or the lucky adopted prize-winning daughter of Charles Francis Adams or the phallic woman (the mother).

His relations to people were characterized by assuming the role he felt he was expected to take. His manner, attitude, speech and mood would vary with each of his friends. He had part object relationships, and his attachment to others con-sisted of being approved.

This gifted boy would repetitively and compulsively try to find a stable, reassuring image of himself, first as the little girl seeking the older masculine man to get his masculinity; then as the phallic mother caring for the defective boy. In order not to have any free time, he would make schedules of things to do and errands to perform. In this way he tried to avoid being frightened and lonely.

In this patient, the symptom formation provides a stable means of reassurance. In this role he is a castrated boy or a girl seeking mother's care, becoming part of her. Both his symptoms and his homosexuality reflect his feminine identi-fication. However, the symptoms, as in the previous case, are intense and mutilating, so that in homosexuality he has a more economical defense against anxiety. His symptoms re-ferring to growing destructive diseases of his lungs and geni-tals reflect pregnancy fantasies indicative of his fear of his identification with women (sister and mother) as passive, castrated figures. In his asymptomatic state, as the active homosexual, he is the active phallic woman, while his object is the defective boy or girl; thereby he possesses the anal penis which the women had taken from the father. Consequently, through this projection acted out, he denies the castrated, passive, destructive identification with women. But the homo-sexuality in itself is self-defeating, for the very act brings anxiety and dissatisfaction in seeking a masculine role.

Summary: Conversion symptoms occur in male homosexuals as direct expression of castration fears reinforced by oral- and anal-sadistic trends resulting from part fixations at the earliest levels of development. The symptom formation represents an identification with the image of the woman (mother) as a passive, castrated figure. Homosexuality appears to be the negative of this symptom formation, namely, a temporary restitutive, anxiety-relieving act, reflecting an active, feminine, phallic identification and serving as a substitute symptom expression. Thus the anal phallus standing for the paternal penis is retained. It would appear that the capacity or level of ego development necessary to withstand the anxiety and tension entailed in giving up homosexuality is essential to successful analysis. Homosexuality itself does not offer the final resolution for anxiety, for it involves denial of reality.

12.

LOSS OF SENSORY PERCEPTION DETERMINING CHOICE OF SYMPTOM

CECIL MUSHATT, M.D.

INTRODUCTION

The frame of reference for this contribution to the study of the transition, "the mysterious leap," from mind to body can be summarized in the words of Felix Deutsch (1940): "Reality (originally) is the person's own body, parts of which are projected in the course of development and objectified, lost so to speak. The loss can only be made good by symbolization of the object and reuniting it again with the body. In restitution, the body functions as if fused with these internal objects. They become forever the internal stimuli." It is hoped that the material to be presented will illustrate and validate the concept of the conversion process put forward in this statement.

In an earlier paper on ulcerative colitis (1954), I showed that the basic problem in this disease can be considered to be a severe depression analogous to melancholia. It was demonstrated how the bowel becomes involved in a conversion process so that it comes to symbolize external objects, especially lost objects, in part or *in toto*, and also those aspects of the individuals themselves which are identified with the external objects. In this way, the bowel no longer functions only according to basic physiological demands but also in accordance with the dynamic relationship of the individual with his external and internal environment, that is, with the external object and its internal representation. The organ then "functions as a symbol of an incorporated object" (Deutsch, 1940).

In this communication I will discuss the case of a twenty-six-year-old unmarried man, whose vision had been greatly impaired since birth as the result of congenital glaucoma, and who sought analysis because of duodenal ulcer with recurrent and frequent hemorrhages. In his fourth year of analysis and after complete freedom from hemorrhage up to this time in analysis he had an acute hemorrhage which necessitated sub-total gastrectomy. This occurred at a very crucial period in the total analytic situation. It was followed by dramatic and substantial progress in behavior both inside and outside of analysis, in personality growth and in his ability to make the fullest use of his limited vision. These changes had previously been taking place only very gradually.

The case will be examined from a number of aspects, namely (1) the nature of the conversion processes and symptoms developed in the eyes and the gastrointestinal tract; (2) the effect of impairment of visual perception on the patient's body-ego organization and on his personality structure; (3) the effect of the impairment of visual perception and of the conversion processes in the eyes in overdetermining the use of the gastrointestinal tract for symbolization of incorporated objects and parts of them; and (4) the effect of such overdetermination on the task faced by the patient in his efforts to reach a state of equilibrium in which he could function successfully in his life.

Anamnesis

The patient first had ulcer symptoms at the age of twenty-one and in the subsequent five years he had six hemorrhages, three of them severe enough to raise the question of the necessity for gastrectomy. The hemorrhages occurred in spring and fall close to times of great significance in his life, all symbolic of separations or losses. Prior to analysis, he had been in psychoanalytically oriented psychotherapy with two successive psychiatrists over a period of two years and simultaneously under active medical care. It had not been found possible to help him to interrupt a progressively deteriorating emotional and physical state.

His other complaints were as follows: (1) gastric pain; and (2) severe anorexia. His diet consisted almost exclusively of coffee and some milk, and the sight of food made him nauseous. It is very likely that malnutrition and exhaustion aggravated his emotional state. (3) He was totally unable to carry on with his career. (4) He was absorbed in compulsive sexual activity both in the form of masturbation and sexual intimacies with girl friends. (5) He spent a great deal of his waking state in apparently purposeless fashion, seeking friends to talk with, and especially at night he could not bear to be alone as a result of which he slept very little. (6) He suffered from severely impaired vision. Consciously the patient did not present his visual difficulties as a reason for analysis. It became clear to him only later that his vision, limited by organic impairment originally, had become reduced still further by psychological processes. In his right eye, which he called his "bad eye," he had vision only for light and movement. In this eye he had a scar which was of considerable concern to him. In his left eye, his "good eye," he had 20/100 vision. He had been told that in his first year of life he had had six operations on his eyes for the construction of channels to permit drainage of intraocular fluid and as a result the glaucoma had become stabilized. His visual ability was still further reduced by a severe bilateral coarse nystagmus which made focusing on objects a difficult task for him. At the time he entered analysis he was having increasing difficulty with his vision. With some effort he could go about his daily activities unaided. Lenses were of use to him only for close work. For reading, though he could see with the aid of special lenses, he required the help of readers, but they, in fact, were becoming of little use to him because he would usually become rapidly lost in fantasies involving them. With one exception, during the greater part of analysis, his readers were all female. He instilled drops in his eyes several times daily. With these drops near objects became clearer, more distant objects became blurred.

The patient was the middle of three boys. His father had held a good position in business but drank heavily. The father had had a club foot and the patient's mother had told him that his father had taken to alcohol because of the son's eyes. The patient himself felt since childhood that his father had been cursed with a club foot and that the curse had been transmitted to him himself in the form of eye defects. There was considerable friction between the parents throughout their marriage with scenes in which the father attacked the mother frequently verbally and on occasion, the patient believed, physically. During his first year of life there were repeated separations from his mother because of hospitalization for operations on his eyes, and during the early years of childhood his father was absent from the home for long periods.

Until after the period in which the gastrectomy took place, there was considerable amnesia for childhood memories and for a great part of analysis only scattered memories were recalled repeatedly. His most frequent childhood recollection was that of his mother bending over him to instill drops in his eyes, a function of his mother's which he himself took over for himself much later as noted. He recalled frequently his visits with his mother for eye examinations, describing often one such occasion when he fainted on overhearing the doctor tell his mother that the prognosis for his eyes was doubtful, expressing in this way the fantasy of complete passivity as the result of blindness. He often expressed the idea that his mother and teachers discouraged him from using his eyes much for fear that visual activity would cause blindness. In school he would often have to depend on classmates to read the blackboard for him, and on occasion he would be given simpler tasks while his classmates went on with their instruction in other subjects. However, apparently in childhood and adolescence, he could cope successfully with his visual handicap in many ways. He could ride a bicycle until he went to high school and in a restricted way he participated in ball games. As he reached puberty, there was indication of increased reluctance to participate in activities with other boys.

During childhood there was a period when he would refuse to eat at meals. This appears to have begun after the birth of his younger brother.

When he was twelve and a half years old his father died from cancer of the throat at the age of forty-eight. During his terminal illness the children would be sent to sit by the father's bedside. Of the scenes witnessed then, the patient could verbalize only his memory of the father's breathing stopping for long periods. The young boy, frightened by this, would be afraid his father would die and at the same time would wish him dead so as to be spared such scenes. The patient felt he never consciously experienced any grief over his father's illness or death. It may be mentioned that he did not recall but one memory of weeping at the age of eight. During analysis weeping occurred only shortly before and after the gastrectomy. Mostly memories of the father in his illness could be recalled only bodily by the patient during analysis, e.g., during analytic hours when he was unconsciously dealing with the period of his life in relation to his father, he would experience choking and gagging sensations. These symptoms were not only derived from fantasies of incorporation of the father and parts of him, but were also a re-enactment of scenes of his father's attacks of choking. These symptoms, it should be added, became condensed with the image of his mother's dyspneic breathing in her terminal illness. She died at age fifty-eight from cardiac failure during the patient's second year of analysis.

Around the time of his father's illness and death, the patient went through a period of secret transvestitism. He became interested in photographing women and chose himself as the model for such pictures. He would dress himself in his mother's clothes and take photographs of himself reflected in the mirror. At such times he would have an erection.

The mother had always spoken bitterly of the father to the children, and during his illness she openly expressed the hope that the father would die. After her husband's death, the mother collapsed in severe depression, became alcoholic like her late husband, and sexually promiscuous. She also developed diabetes. The children would often come home to find the mother on the floor, stuporous and incoherent and crying out, "Daddy, why did you leave me?" and "Do something." The patient for a considerable time could not verbalize his recollection of these scenes clearly, but in the transference strikingly re-enacted them as he tossed about on the couch talking sleepily and disjointedly, attacking the analyst for failing him and angrily demanding of the analyst to do something. The patient would frequently overhear his mother at night in her sexual activities in the home with men friends from whom she stole money on occasion. The patient felt he could not go to sleep until his mother was either safe at home or quiet in her bed.

The patient's relationship with his brothers was very close and ambivalent. His older brother had a peptic ulcer but kept it under control with medical treatment. This brother, to whom the patient was deeply attached, he both admired and resented for his professional success, and especially he resented him for his marriage which took place several months before the patient's first hemorrhage. The patient was extremely jealous of his sister-in-law, and among other events occurring around the time of his second hemorrhage was the fact of his sister-in-law's becoming pregnant. The two brothers had slept together for a number of years in childhood, and at this time the patient had enjoyed sleeping behind his brother and in close bodily contact. Toward his younger brother he maintained a protective attitude at the same time as he was extremely jealous of him. The patient resented both brothers as well as his father and later his mother's men friends because they disrupted the intimate relationship which he felt he had had with his mother because of his eyes.

The patient apparently did quite well in grade school and high school. In spite of a great deal of guilt over leaving his mother at a time when he felt she needed help, he went to college and did well there until in his final year he began to have gastric symptoms. In his undergraduate years he would repeatedly find it necessary to leave college for home "To help his mother out of scrapes." Soon after embarking on preparations for his career at a considerable distance from his mother, he began to break down rapidly.

From the point of view of the present study, these were the highlights of conscious anamnestic material presented gradually by the patient. Undoubtedly, considerable distortion of external facts took place especially because of the patient's extreme readiness to fantasize which developed in him as a result of his impaired capacity adequately to perceive events visually.

ANALYTIC OBSERVATIONS

Central Problem, Including Remarks on Body Image

For the purpose of introducing the analytic observations, the first two analytic hours will be summarized. In the first hour, the patient started by saying that he wanted to curl up into a little ball, to retreat from the world and say "To hell with the world." He felt guilty over masturbation and over his thoughts about women. "It's the kind of women I portray, all strange." At this point the patient had his eyes closed and he sounded as if he were going off to sleep. When his attention was drawn to this, he remarked, "With my eyes closed, I am away from everything. I get a lump in my throat and a warm sensation in my stomach when I think of my college girl friend. In my childhood, I would lie awake nights swallowing." Then he went on to express his hatred for two male friends, emphasizing that one of them was married so that he himself would not be suspected of being homosexual. He talked then of his first seeking psychiatric help and of how while during vacation and staying with his older brother (who had just recently married) he learned that his "Young psychiatrist" had left the community unexpectedly. He felt nothing about this latter event, but remarked on the fact that one month later he had had his first hemorrhage.

He began his second hour by remarking that he thought he was late. He felt he had inherited his mother's being late. She was invariably late to meet his father at the train. Subsequently he went on to say, "It's warm here and I feel comfortable. It feels good to know I shall be able to talk to you every day. Just now my stomach and head are in shape. I feel kind of open. I can cope with anything that comes in to fill up the hole. I feel like a battleship well prepared, guns ready."

This summary of the first two hours is presented here because, as it turned out, the patient unconsciously outlined in these hours the whole course of his analysis, the dynamic basis for his severe character disorder, and for his ulcer and hemorrhages. He indicated here, too, the effect which his defective vision had on the development of his body image and on his personality, and the effect it had in channeling symbolization processes into the gastrointestinal tract. These remarks will become clearer in the ensuing discussion.

His behavior in his first analytic hour with his hostile withdrawal from the realities of life characterized the patient's behavior throughout the greater part of his analysis and in his life outside. On the couch, he talked mostly in a sleepy, extremely irritable and frequently disjointed and almost incoherent fashion. In his life outside of analysis, with men he was hostile in the extreme, and with women he was both hostile and inordinately demanding. Through the latter he appeared to be trying to live a vicarious existence. He gave the impression of having little sense of identity of his own, and it soon became obvious that relationships were established on a primitive oral level in which instinctual and ego behavior were not clearly differentiated. In this connection it is significant that for a considerable time the patient insisted that he could find solutions to all his problems through sexual activities, as a result of which a great part of his daily life was given over to masturbation and sexual activities with girl friends.

In this primitive state, he was all mouth, all cavity. This was described simply by the patient in various ways, e.g., (1) "The only thing that has reality for me is my mouth"; (2) "I met Dr. J. I would pick him for a father. In comparison with him I felt hollow, not occupying space"; (3) "I feel kind of open. I can cope with anything that comes in to fill up the hole" (see second analytic hour).

What ego activities appeared in the early part of analysis were dependent on his transference relationship in which he felt that what he did in the direction of ego striving was for the analyst's benefit, and that he was only an instrument in the service of the analyst. He felt that the analyst and he were one. In this respect can be mentioned that happy memories of childhood were expressed repeatedly in the recollection of himself in the playroom downstairs with his brothers building model airplanes, feeling peaceful in the knowledge that his mother was upstairs working. Frequently during analysis he could apply himself to his studies only while a girl friend was present with him, or when he had the fantasy that a girl friend was present and watching him. In circumstances in which he felt completely dependent, he felt not only secure, as indicated in the second analytic hour, but even invulnerable. "I used to have a feeling of indestructibility and I could keep working as long as I ate and got some sleep. Then after I got my ulcer I changed my view . . . It's cold here, I am angry." (He apparently felt his dependency on the analyst threatened at this point.) He was continually preoccupied with fears of death, and understandably, as will be seen, he felt that his very existence was at stake. It will become clear from the discussion below that by his regression he was trying desperately to save himself by an effort to reestablish in fantasy his original identity. The disintegration of his mother destroyed the symbiotic relationship through which he functioned. This was aggravated by the death of his father at a critical period in the patient's life as well as by the subsequent identification through the symbiotic relationship that followed with his disintegrated mother. In this disruption of his symbiotic state with his healthy mother, he was continually afraid he would starve and die. He was hungry for a suitable dependent and symbiotic relationship and complete identification or merging with the object.

Food and individuals in whole or part became identical to the patient. Obsessive preoccupation with searching for friends took the place of meals, and at meals he could not eat because of his conscious and preconscious oral incorporative fantasies in relation to his companions. Here may be mentioned the frequently recalled childhood experience, when in school he would become absorbed in looking at his female teacher's legs and become panicked at the thought of death, as he fantasied himself merging with one of her legs.

The fantasy of symbiotic merging with the object was like a threat of death, while the fantasy of the object merging with him threatened him with the destruction of the object. At the same time separation from the object was like a threat of death to him. He felt thus in an insoluble dilemma. He sought a primitively infantile dependent state and at the same time had to deny to himself dependency on others, and in doing so had to deny himself food.

He thus fluctuated between two pictures of himself, (1) completely helpless and passive, and (2) completely independent and omnipotent. Both pictures were manifestations of his symbiotic state. In the former position it turned out that he viewed himself as an infant girl, completely helpless, blind and castrated, destructive and castrating, and demanding fulfillment of all her wishes. This was the picture too of his mother after her disintegration, and the picture of himself after the breakdown of his symbiotic relationship with his healthy mother. As his mother demanded of the world, he angrily demanded of the analyst and his friends the restoration of a symbiotic relationship with the fantasy that this could be achieved by gratification in concrete form of his oral sexual wishes, just as he fantasied his mother on her part had acted them out after her husband's death. The fantasied fulfillment of such a relationship with the analyst provided him with the other view of himself. In this latter position he was an omnipotent superseeing phallic girl. This view of himself belongs to the period when he looked upon his mother as a strong, large-breasted phallic woman, when his symbiotic relationship with her was intact, and when, as he described it in connection with a transference figure, "He could jump into her skin and see through her eyes." If this fantasy were realized, he could deny the disintegration of his mother, and the death of his father; he could be free of this extreme guilt toward both his mother and father and his brothers; he could erase the memory of his bitter disappointments, and he

could be free of his unrelenting hostility. His efforts at restitution of his original image of himself and thus at re-establishing his sense of identity are best seen from the following
summary of the analysis of his compulsive sexual activities.

He masturbated by rubbing his nipples. His main conscious fantasy was that of a strong, large-breasted woman,
fully dressed, pinning him down and forcing one of her
breasts into his mouth at the same time as she pressed her
thigh against his penis. This fantasy was especially prominent during the period in analysis when his mother was having recurrent attacks of heart failure, when she seemed likely
to die during one of them. The patient could rarely speak
of his concern about his mother at these times. The fantasy
was an activation of the fantasy aroused in him in childhood
when his mother would bend over him to put drops in his
eyes. For the instant of that act he felt that his mother was
his, meaning on a deep level as he said in describing his
dancing with a girl whom he identified with his mother, "She
was mine, the whole system belonged to me and was me. She
became the aggressive womanly part of me." As a result of
the drops, near objects became bigger and he had greater
visual power. This gave him a sense, too, of greater phallic
power (see below). Thus in the masturbation fantasy he fantasied himself becoming his mother when she was healthy, a
phallic but castrating woman. His mother as a phallic woman
was reinforced by his equation of penis and breast and of
the eyedropper and penis (see later). It may be recalled here
that in his first analytic hour, after speaking of "the kind of
women I portray" with his eyes closed, that is unseeing, he
thought of a girl whom he identified later with his healthy
mother and the revival of whose image gave him a good
feeling, a lump in his throat and a warm sensation in his
stomach. This recalled his compulsive swallowing in childhood, that is, his oral incorporative fantasies. This in turn
led to associations of resentment against brother figures and

his first hemorrhage on separation from the psychiatrist. He regarded psychiatrists, it may be added, as maternal figures.

In his sexual intimacies with women, he maintained friendships with a number of women simultaneously. He divided them into those who were strong, identified with his mother before her breakdown, and those who were sexually promiscuous, alcoholic or severely depressed like his mother after her breakdown. He was more strongly attracted to the latter group. With the strong women he saw himself mainly as a child demanding of sympathy and comfort. The other type of women he viewed as demanding of him, and he saw himself in the role of their rescuer, going to their aid at any time of day or night to comfort them and soothe them by intercourse or fellatio. "It was an emergency that excused me from my daily work." With the strong women, in their moments of vulnerability, he would see himself in the same role. Consciously he regarded these activities as a demonstration of his manliness, and on the surface they appeared to be an acting out of his oedipal fantasies for which there had been enormous provocation during his adolescence arising from his mother's drunkenness and promiscuity, as well as in childhood when the father would charge the mother with premarital promiscuity. In adolescence he had conscious sexual fantasies of dreams involving his mother with profound guilt over them. He was profoundly guilty over his conscious efforts to see his mother nude and to touch her. These fantasies, consciously interpreted by him in their significance as oedipal in origin, he brought into juxtaposition with his father's death and his sense of responsibility for it. No doubt on this level of meaning alone, the fantasies contributed heavily to the development of conversion symptoms in his eyes, namely his increasing disability to use his already organically damaged eyes and his nystagmus. He referred to himself as "Little Oedipus."

These oedipal fantasies, however, served largely as a defense against his more profound preoedipal fantasies. They had the effect too of greatly intensifying his regression out of guilt. He entered the oedipal period and puberty in an inverted position, with little capacity to cope with the oedipal conflict. For instance, the greatest source of guilt over scoptophilic activities came from his oral incorporative fantasies associated with looking at (and touching) his mother, and from his oral fantasies when in childhood he saw his father urinate. As it turned out, his guilt toward his father was largely the guilt of his mother. Behind his conscious effort to portray himself as a phallic man in his sexual activities with women were two sets of fantasies: (1) the fantasy of orally introjecting the woman, especially her breasts and of becoming the phallic woman comforting the frightened and castrated little girl, providing her at one and the same time with the breast and penis. This was a central unconscious fantasy with the alcoholic and depressed women. (2) The fantasy of himself being the blind, unhappy, helpless and castrated little girl comforted by the phallic woman whom he fantasied introjecting. These two sets of fantasies as well as his masturbation fantasies were expressions of the same process, namely the effort to re-establish the original image of himself, by restoring within himself the original image of his mother. His acting out of his rescue fantasies was not only a representation of the fantasied rescue of his mother, but also an attempt to rescue himself from disintegration after the disruption of his symbiotic relationship with the mother which resulted from her breakdown. It represented also an attempt to rescue himself from his identification with his disintegrated mother.

This interpretation of the patient's sexual activities gains support from the fact that the patient described the fantasy that he was originally a phallic girl. "Everyone starts out as a girl and later boys are made." He had become a weak (castrated) ugly girl because his eyes were ugly. He brought material repeatedly to show that unconsciously he felt that his fantasy of himself as a girl had come about as a result of his eyes. For example, "If I close my eyes I'll turn into a woman," that is, unseeing or blind he becomes a woman. And again, "The girl thing comes from my eyes. My eyes are bad. I have a picture of a little kid struggling, not seeing where he is going, lost and helpless. The girl is helpless. The guy who can't see is helpless. He needs someone there to lead him around. When I was a kid I had nightmares thinking something was pursuing me, and I was not able to get away. Darkness would close in, and I couldn't move my arms or legs and I couldn't scream for mother. The terror in that is similar to being left alone. Death, how suddenly everything ceases, all alone and there is nobody. I am afraid of being without Mary [his girl friend]. I want to have a girl around into whose skin I can jump, to look at the world from her point of view, even from her eyes. What I am afraid of then is giving up the girl in me." Behind this material lay the fantasy of acquiring or inheriting his mother's eyes, and the failure of his mother to give him her eyes not only after her death but before it was an unconscious source of extreme resentment toward his mother. He expressed in this way through the symbiotic relationship his fantasy of total identification with the woman, his mother. His view of his father as an orally fixated, defective and weak man only served to reinforce this identification.

The same fantasy of himself was expressed very clearly in terms of his body image, in the Cyclops fantasy which he revealed six months after the gastrectomy. A male friend had remarked that his eyes no longer shook as much as before. The patient associated to the fantasy of himself as something super with a unique mind. The left half of his mind out of which he saw was sensitive, and the right out of which he did not see lay dormant. Seeing out of the left eye made the left side sensitive. If he could see out of his right eye, he would be powerful. He wanted the doctors to remove the scar in his right eye to make them look symmetrical. (This would have made the eye completely blind, equivalent to his having only one eye.) He went on as follows: "I want to tilt my head to the right, all of me to the right to compensate, to get my left eyeball right in the center. I think of a guy with a powerful eye in the middle of his head, sees all, knows all and he has a great big penis. I picture myself powerful, surveying the world and doing a systematic sweep of the environment. I have been told that my eyeball shaking is due to a continuous search process—to the extent that I can hold one of the spots in front of my eye steady my eyes do not shake." Then he described a fantasy that his penis had been cut off and he was terribly weak. He followed this with the story of David hitting Goliath in the middle of the forehead. In this Cyclops fantasy he is all left side and powerful but vulnerable. During the period of analysis in which he brought this material, he described fantasies of himself as an "Angry, potent female," the "Battleship with guns ready." Analytic material showed that he equated his left side and left "good" eye with his mother. His right side and his right "bad" eye he equated with his father with his clubfoot, the side of him of which he wanted to rid himself as his mother had wanted to do. The Cyclops eye is a phallus, but the female phallus and vulnerable. If he had had a good right eye, a strong phallic father, he would have been truly powerful, identified with the phallic man and the phallic woman symbolized by David with his "V-shaped sling and stone." In the Cyclops fantasy, it may be added, he demonstrates with the fantasy of his body image the irreconcilable antagonism between mother and father, taking sides completely with the mother and trying to reject the defective father. One source of danger to life lay in this fantasy of achieving complete identification with the mother.

The Eyes

At this point the conversion processes and symptoms in the eyes will be discussed in some detail.

Reference has already been made to the symbolizations of the mother and father in his eyes. The following material, for instance, exemplifies the equation of the scarred right eye with his clubfooted father. In an hour during the fifth year of analysis, when the patient "was crying like mother" over the death of his father and expressing his anger at his father for not taking care of him and at the same time expressing his mother's devaluation of the father, he said he wanted to pluck out his right eye and went on, "I really don't want to cry about my father, I don't like him. I want to cry about myself. I want to put a half dollar over my right eye. I can't see except with my left eye. That's the thing to cry about. My right eye, the bad eye, is teary." Thus, through his eyes and their symbolizations he could express the antagonism between his mother and father.

Predominantly in the stage of analysis prior to the changes occurring around the time of the gastrectomy, he equated his eyes with those of a helpless, castrated girl, who used her eyes only for being beautiful. Such a girl received impressions through her eyes without having to act on them of her own accord. She had to be led by the man. She could use her eyes aggressively and destructively by grasping the object and not as strong people did by penetrating the object with their gaze. In this sense, his eyes became highly sexualized and equated with parts of the passive girl, mouth, anus, and vagina. To him all these hollow organs were the same. The sexualization of the eyes became especially clear in the analysis of the scenes of his mother putting drops into his eyes, and in the analysis of his guilt over seeing his father urinate. Thus in an hour shortly before termination of analysis, he said, "The night before last I masturbated and I think now of putting drops in my eyes. I have a picture of holding the eyedropper over my eyes and a picture of my masturbating. When I was a kid, my mother used to put my eyes in, I mean my eyedrops in. As if she were saying, 'Your eyes are in. You can see for a while.' When I put my drops in, my eyes feel refreshed. I feel things are bigger and I have greater visual power. I want to think of a similarity between eyedropper and penis. I want to think of my mother giving me my penis and it belongs to me. For me eyes and penis are confused. Sexual power has to do with seeing far. . . . I think of my mother putting drops in my eyes. I keep thinking of the eyedropper plunging into my eyeballs through a thin membrane and the whole thing comes open and liquid and pus and blood come out. I think of a story about the octopus which I know is not true. It grabs its prey and pulls it against a long tooth in its head. I think of someone doing something to the octopus's eye to stop it from killing. I think of my mother putting drops in my eyes. For that instant she was mine. The eye doctor had a hard time trying to put the instrument for measuring tension on my eyes. My eyeball would move around so fast. I always felt it was running away from the instrument. When my mother put drops in I never had this sweating out. I felt she was more competent. How could she put the eyedropper so close to my eyes without touching them? I wanted her to put the eyedropper in my eyeball. I wanted my mother to have a penis and to screw me. I feel nervous. I have a fantasy of reaching out and grabbing my mother and pulling her on top of me." The relation of this material to the patient's dominant masturbation fantasy described earlier is clear. There can be seen well in this material the patient's equation of his eyes with the mouth and vagina, both incorporative and castrating organs, and from this material together with the masturbation fantasy already described can be seen the equation of the eyedropper

with his mother's fantasied penis and with her breast, both
becoming his own.

In regard to the latter remark, some further material
may be added. In an earlier hour the patient remarked,
"Tears come out of my eyes, and I feel I am losing my drops,
I better go and put my drops in." This material in itself
demonstrates how the drops became part of himself, and
taken together with the material quoted earlier can be regarded as showing how the drops became equated with his
mother, her breast and penis, and then with the patient
himself. In crying at this time over his father he was not
only expressing his identification with his mother, but expressed his readiness to separate from his attachment and
identification with her, and his fear of doing so.

The eye equated with the mouth as well as the prohibition
against looking and seeing because of passive receptive fantasies regarding the father is illustrated in the following
material: "As a kid, I would put my finger over my good eye.
Mother and father would ask if it hurt. I would say, 'I was
just sitting like this.' The main effort was not to see. Not
seeing is a screwy way of having seen something I don't want
to see. Naked bodies aren't nice, they are hairy. I think of my
father in the bathroom urinating and I had to stand and
look up at that. At dinner we had glasses with a picture of a
kid urinating into the fountain. Urinating and taking a
drink, doesn't this have to do with my wanting to take a
drink from father's penis? I think of a kid grabbing the old
man's leg, and reaching up and kissing his penis and saying,
'Daddy don't go away.' I understand my wanting to offer my
mother a drink."

During the greater part of the analysis phallic representation of the eyes was poorly developed and repressed. It is
felt that this was due not only to the organic impairment in
the eyes but even more so was caused by the representations
of orally organized family figures and parts of them in the

eyes together with conversion symptoms expressive of conflict of the patient in his relationship to these figures. Function of the eyes under the influence of phallic representation began to appear only shortly before and dramatically after the gastrectomy. It will be shown how the phase of analysis in which the operation occurred was one of massive effort by the patient to renounce his pathological identifications.

When phallic representation did appear, his good eye was equated with the female phallus, as seen in the Cyclops fantasy and in the material presented above regarding his fantasies about the instillation of the eyedrops. The female phallus he described as a circumcised penis. He himself was circumcised and he regarded the circumcised penis as "a feminine thing" as compared with the uncircumcised penis which was "big and masculine." It is of interest that this concept of the patient's is a reversal of the usual concept of the uncircumcised penis as a symbol of bisexuality, and the circumcised penis as a symbol of masculinity alone (Nunberg, 1949). His own eyes he equated with the circumcised penis, and undoubtedly this explained his idea of the circumcised penis as feminine. He had fantasied asking an oculist for a small plastic thing to put over both eyes to make them look alike, saying that "All handicapped people have a castration complex." In the same hour as he described the fantasy of the circumcised penis as female, he described the fantasy of himself as an attractive but castrating woman— "Wanting to borrow some of his boss's skin, his foreskin" which he equated with the acquisition of some of his boss's wisdom and power. As already shown the patient described a sense of confusion between visual ability and phallic power. It may be mentioned here that he described the fantasy of his body as a phallus but usually it was as the phallus of his mother or representatives of her.

The nystagmus had a number of determinants for him, namely: (1) as an expression of ambivalence in identifications, of his inability to achieve a reconciliation between the active and passive, masculine and feminine sides of himself. This is indirectly expressed in the Cyclops material, and more explicitly stated in the following material from an hour early in analysis: "I was having dinner with Mike and Charlie. I felt nauseous. I felt I could not be with two people at once. I had to concentrate on one or the other unless there are more than two. Like my brothers, it's the idea of being stuck between two people—In my left eye, the one I see out of, there is a tremor. When I go to focus on anything it shakes around. This must have to do with the way I think—I must have subjects (= objects subjected to him) for my work and I am scared to go into the plant to ask for subjects." (2) As an expression of the sexualization of his eyes and the prohibition against oral introjective fantasies, against aggressive holding and aggressive penetration of the object. With his nystagmus he could see only in a passive way and in effect could deny active looking and seeing. (3) As an expression of avoidance of homosexual attack, as when he described his eyes as running away from the ophthalmologist's instrument. (4) As symbolic of himself as the powerful, phallic, castrating female seeking control. This is expressed, for example, in the content of the Cyclops fantasy. His description of his eyes shaking corresponds closely with his description of his fantasy of the phallic, castrating female on top of the man with her vaginal muscles moving back and forth while the man lay still.

Thus it can be seen the eyes functioned not only in the service of visual perception but physiologically they were also under the influence of symbolizations and conversion symptoms with the result that vision was impaired greatly beyond that due to organic damage.

The Gastrointestinal Tract

The immense amount of material bearing on the gastrointestinal tract can be summarized as follows.

Reference has already been made to the patient's view of himself as all mouth, all cavity. In this primitive state, comparable to Simmel's "gastrointestinal phase" (1944), the object became himself and he became the object. Parts of the object were parts of himself and parts of himself were parts of the object. Parts became equated with the whole and organs became equated with whole objects, with the corresponding or other parts of the object. Thus, through his gastrointestinal tract, he came to symbolize external objects, part of these objects, the dynamic relationships of himself with objects and of objects with objects, and the functions of other individual parts of himself and of the object. The stomach was predominantly equated with the mother, and the ulcerated and painful stomach with the mother during her breakdown. It also became a representation of his father and of his brothers and of himself, as well as oral, anal, and genital representations of all. Frequently it was difficult to separate out these representations from each other. They would seem fused, just as he felt that he "had difficulty in differentiating between a mother and father in the same situation." In its predominant symbolization of his mother, both healthy and after her breakdown, the stomach became a representation of himself "dependent as a woman" who when disappointed, deserted or having to take responsibility became orally demanding, destructive and castrating. Through his stomach he could portray on the one hand his identification with his mother and his dependence on her, and on the other hand his fight to assert his independence of her to assert his masculine side. He could portray relationships between his mother and father and the antagonism between the two, expressing thus the irreconcilability of the male and the female sides of himself. Through his stomach he could symbolize parts of the mother and father, namely, the mouth, anus, and genitalia, using the parts as symbols for the whole person and portraying through the parts the relationship between the mother, the father, and other men. Through his gastrointestinal tract he could express his mother's grief and the grief of himself in his identification with her over the death of the father. He could express his mother's and his own bitterness and aggression toward the father and the world, and his father's and his own aggression toward his mother and the world. He could portray his identification with and his resentment toward his brothers.

He was immobilized by his stomach in a passive, feminine position against which he tried to protest, but the protest and threats of the stomach representing his mother, his feminine self, were too great. At times he would personify his stomach and attack it for holding him back from activity, just as his stomach would attack him for his activity. In his position of dependency, under pressure from his stomach he would continually quote his mother's words spoken to him, namely, "You are entitled to help. Fight for your right because of your eyes." The painful stomach was the protest of his mother against his leaving her, against his abandoning his identification with her, as his mother had protested against his father leaving her. As his mother protested against threats to her dependence and against separation, he could echo the same protest with his stomach, even threatening to symbolize the separations with bleeding, as when the analyst was about to leave on vacation and he remarked, "I have a feeling of being alone. I am afraid I shall bleed." And he actually did bleed, for instance when his older brother deserted him by his marriage at the same time as his first therapist left him. He bled on one occasion close to the birthday of his younger brother which symbolized for him originally separation from his mother.

When he could achieve a passive dependent relationship, or rather a fantasied symbiotic relationship with little accomplished in terms of ego development, his stomach would be at rest. His stomach pain would cease when he masturbated, conjuring up oral sexual fantasies, just as he fantasied that his mother would have been made peaceful by his gratifying her oral wishes in concrete sexual terms. But when he was in a passive state, he would attack his passive feminine self with his stomach pain just as his father would attack his mother, or as his father would attack him for his passivity in childhood. The attack on the mother and on the mother in him was also represented in him by the jabbing of his father's penis which he fantasied incorporated into his stomach. In this way, too, he could portray through his stomach the fantasied violence of intercourse between his mother and father and other men echoing his mother's words, "Ooh, it hurts." In this connection he also fantasied his stomach as the female genitalia containing the hidden female phallus. Impregnation fantasies and fantasies of menstruation from the stomach were frequently described by the patient.

Pain in the stomach, as indicated, was a frequent expression of aggression, and it appeared most frequently in connection with oral cannibalistic fantasies.

Through his vomiting he could express rejection or expulsion of the object, that is, separation from the object and from his identification with the object. For instance, on one occasion he had been talking of his resentment when an older woman whose favorite he had felt himself to be, had shown interest in a male friend of his. He remarked that he never got his feelings toward his brothers explicit and then went on to say, "It's down here in my chest and in my stomach above my bellybutton. It's pushing away (forward) from there. This is the part that got the ulcers. I have the image of a little kid spitting and vomiting in the direction of his brothers and saying, 'I don't want them, get them away.' My brothers and I were close and not close, liking and not liking are part of the same thing." Through his vomiting he could also express phallic and anal aggression and the violence of his father who had attacked the mother. Thus, when once he complained of a desire to vomit, he revealed the fantasy of smashing the analyst with an axe and of sleeping with women instead of murdering them. "I think of me with the axe smashing you, the blood and my vomiting and shitting at the same time. I am aware of my penis now and I think of pushing it out and ejaculating white stuff. The stomach and the shit will be the same stuff as inside you. The act of retching and of throwing the axe are the same. I think of vomiting over people." In addition, the patient expressed his grief and crying by vomiting. Thus, in the first analytic hour after the operation he remarked, "I want to stick my finger in my mouth and cry like hell. Tears actually came into my eyes. I think of me in a blue sweater that my mother knitted and of the dried-up kid who couldn't cry. I'm amazed at the closeness I came to bawling. I'm glad you are here, I can't cry by myself. I am liable to throw up. But that's not true any more." Ten months after gastrectomy, on the anniversary of his father's death, he cried bitterly over his father and remarked, "I thought I can't cry because my stomach would burst. You are it. I can't count on my brothers. I feel I am leaving you. I am talking like my mother. She cried over my father but got nowhere. Instead of crying I want to gag and vomit. It centers around my throat." Through his vomiting he could express his mother's and his own grief and bitterness over the father's death and also, it may be mentioned, his grief over his father's terminal illness, "It centers around my throat." The vomiting, like his crying, was expressive of his effort to separate himself from his mother and father and from his identification with them. All bodily functions, namely, crying, vomiting, defecation, and ejaculation, were equated and were expressions not only of destruction of the object but of expulsion of the incorporated object, that is, separation from identification with the object. The latter process was seen by the patient as symbolic of destruction of the object, and while he maintained these identifications he could feel the objects were alive. In connection with the equation of vomiting and ejaculation may be mentioned the fantasies described postoperatively by the patient, namely that his stomach had been a penis, and that his stomach contained his father's penis.

It becomes quite clear from this material that like the eyes the stomach functioned very little according to basic physiological demands but to an extreme degree under the influence of the need to express symbolizations and conversion symptoms.

Further Discussion of the Course of the Analysis

The hemorrhage and gastrectomy. In the forty-fourth month of analysis the patient had a severe gastric hemorrhage and subtotal gastrectomy had to be performed. The hemorrhage occurred at a time of massive significance for him. He had just completed the final procedures for fulfillment of the requirements for a position which would have started him on his career. These steps had been postponed for a very considerable time. The initial definitive steps were taken about one month after the anniversary of the death of his mother, while the requirements were completed within one month of the anniversary of the death of his father. In this period, too, a token separation from the analyst had taken place as the result of a reduction of the frequency of analytic sessions which it had been hoped would facilitate his tolerance and his progress in analysis. It may be stated that he had always consciously viewed the taking of definitive steps in regard to his career as a move toward final separation from the analyst whom he viewed mainly as a maternal figure up to this time, together with the relinquishing of his profound and passive feminine identification and of his dependency. The sources of difficulty for him in making such a transition will soon become evident.

In addition to the above, during the month preceding the

hemorrhage he had been having an extremely difficult time with abdominal pain, vomiting and dizziness. During this time he had become consistently articulate for virtually the first time in analysis. It was obvious that he was making a strenuous effort to externalize his life experiences and fantasies through verbalization instead of through nonverbal bodily language, in order to free himself of his pathological identifications and of his fixation in symbiotic relationships. In this month and the several preceding months he had been able to uncover and analyze in detail his oral, cannibalistic fantasies. There now broke through a strenuous effort to face with appropriate mourning the death of his mother and father as well as his feelings about his mother's pathological behavior after the death of the father. He mourned for himself and for his mother over the death of his father—"I feel the kind of upset that my mother felt over my father's death." At the same time he recognized that he could neither save himself nor his mother by identifying with her, especially as she was when she was ill.

The meaning of the hemorrhage and gastrectomy in the context of analysis in which it occurred can be summarized as follows. At the time of the hemorrhage, in his apartment there was blood everywhere—"It looked like a murder had been done, my own murder." It had looked to him as if the only thing that could have been done about his father's death was that he himself should die. He had always felt that had his father lived, he would never have been able to go to college. He had consciously hoped his father would die in order that he could go to college. At the same time his mother interfered greatly with his life at college and he had consciously wished her dead too. In other words, he could pursue his own plans for his career undisturbed and he could go on with his life only if he could rid himself of his identifications with his mother and father and of his guilt toward both. These processes were obviously viewed by the patient as a psychological suicide. It can be seen here that with the patient expressing psychological representations in such concrete terms as was observed in him, that there had been the danger of organic suicide, as indicated above, and again in the remark: "If I don't die of ulcers I'll die of heart failure" (like his mother). Sufficient work was accomplished in analysis so that he came to limit this to the concrete sacrifice of his stomach rather than of his total self.

Later in analysis, he identified his ulcerated stomach with "the dirty side of himself," and this in turn with his mother whom his father had called a whore. In the same hour he associated this side of himself and his mother with a woman whom he fantasied to be homosexual, revealing thus his unconscious understanding of the mother's promiscuity. It is of further significance that immediately after the operation he had a hallucinatory-like experience in which he kept telling himself that he was not his mother. He had been thinking that he was his mother, sick in hospital in her terminal cardiac illness, and he had pain in his back as she had then. He kept reaching under himself as if to try to pluck off green gangrenous stuff, as he had witnessed his mother do with her bed sores. The duodenal ulcer had been shifted now, but only as a fantasied ulcer to the outside of his body. In addition he told of his fantasy postoperatively, that he had had his father's penis inside, indestructible and removable only by cutting it out. It is probably of significance here that in the ulcer scar was found a relatively large fibrous nodule. He revealed in this way his unconscious fantasy of the source of his mother's guilt toward the father, namely, that she had castrated the father, and his fantasy of having done so himself. On behalf of her and himself, he was making restitution to the father.

Chiefly then, the hemorrhage and the concrete abandonment of the stomach were symbolic of his impending abandonment of his identification with his mother in her state of disintegration, of making peace with his father, and of abandoning his identification with his father as the weak, castrated man.

Postgastrectomy period. The change in the patient after the period of analysis climaxed by the hemorrhage and gastrectomy was striking. A significant change had been gradually making its appearance in the few months before the hemorrhage, but now it had become dramatic. He reported that he already felt the change when he woke up from the anesthetic. His convalescence was rapid and without the usual postgastrectomy symptoms. The change was a fundamental one, accompanied by a striking alteration in behavior inside and outside of analysis and by sustained movement in analysis. He described the change as his rebirth. He now gave the appearance of a person with a sense of his own individuality in the process of abandoning to a marked degree his pregenital organization with its oral and anal possessiveness, aggression and destructiveness, and no longer seeking a symbiotic relationship with the analyst. His infantile, oral, cannibalistic fantasies were now being left behind. Thus, in the first analytic hour three weeks after the operation, he recalled the preoperative fantasy of himself as a dinosaur eating up every part of the analyst except his penis, and he went on to say how well he had been eating since the operation, especially meat, eating it with his hands, that now he must eat in a civilized fashion. He recalled his childhood inhibitions about eating, saying, "When I lie here talking of my childhood eating I feel like an idiot. It is too far away from real life." He spoke now of his pride in his sense of manliness, limited though he felt it to be, and of his reduced sense of guilt. "All my bones and muscles stand out. I think of myself as clean and I can get healthy." He now expressed his emotions appropriately, his happiness as well as his anger and sadness, and he expressed them quite freely. Both verbally and physically he acted more vigorously. Whereas previously he was continually unkempt, unshaven and shabbily dressed, he now consistently appeared well groomed. In a number of ways he began to express overtly his efforts at identification with the analyst, and this showed itself notice-ably in his manner of dress.

From this time on he became much less afraid of associa-tions with men. In fact, he could now not only enjoy men's company, but especially in his work he could now learn from both his male superiors and peers, where previously associa-tion with men and learning from them by identification were blocked by his fear of homosexuality and by the fantasy of destruction of the object associated for him with identifica-tion. At the same time his compulsive masturbation and other compulsive sexual activities virtually disappeared. His relationships with women were markedly changed. His object relations assumed a more genital character.

Very striking were the facts that now he could eat well and normally, he could talk freely in analysis, and he could now read unrestrictedly with the aid of glasses. His nystagmus became greatly reduced and at times imperceptible. He aban-doned the use of readers entirely. Thus it can be said that he could now use his eyes in a more phallic sense; and as a derivative of this, he could take a more active part in the examination of his associations making his own penetrating observations and without having to wait for the analyst's inter-pretations to the same extent as before, that is, without wait-ing to see through the analyst's eyes. He could also now ex-press his grief through crying which can be regarded also as an expression of the appearance of previously absent and inhibited phallic representation in the eyes, though in a female sense in this respect. His readiness to speak freely and to associate freely appear to have the same phallic and masculine implication. As already described, he spoke pre-viously in a sleepy, disconnected fashion. Early in analysis he described his difficulty in associating to the fact that his mother when drunk would become "alogical. Her thoughts would jump around and lose order," just as he "jumped around babbling illogically like an idiot." On another occasion he compared free association to a limitless waterfall which on one level seemed to be an allusion to his father's urinary stream as compared to his mother's "babbling."

The emphasis in the material after the gastrectomy and subsequently was thus on a shift to a more masculine identification in all aspects of his body image, to a representation of himself as more masculine and less the inadequate, helpless and orally demanding woman. However, it needs to be made clear that the material showed that this was so in the sense that now he saw himself as a phallic girl and no longer the blind, castrated girl he had become. He had begun to rid himself to a great extent of his identification with his sick mother and he now saw himself more in the image of his mother as he had viewed her when she was healthy. In this sense he had been reborn, reborn in the original image of his fantasy that all start out as (phallic) girls and later boys are made. It is clear that the latter fantasy had its origin in the fantasy of complete identification or unity with the mother in the original infant-mother symbiotic relationship. In this state he had become fixated, as a result in large part, I believe, of the impairment of vision through the conversion processes developed in the eyes, with the effect which these processes had in making the identification with a whole family of orally organized and castrated (= hollow, feminine) figures so profound. With the appearance of phallic representation in the eyes, bringing with it a return of so much more visual ability and with the release from identification with such figures symbolized in part by the sacrifice of his stomach, together with the mastery of his primitive, oral incorporative fantasies, he could begin to separate himself out more clearly and to make new identifications. For instance, he began to see the analyst as a more masculine and paternal figure and less as a maternal figure. Facilitated by his newly acquired capacity for identification without so much fear of destruction of the object, he could now begin to detach himself from his predominant identification with his healthy mother and make masculine identifications, e.g., with the analyst. There appeared indications during this period of his analysis of his regard for his father's capabilities as well as expression of his childhood fantasy of reconciling mother and father, thus trying to reconcile them within himself. In this way he could express his shift to becoming more masculine and less feminine. He began to show a greater capacity for independent activity, and he no longer asked continually for a mother in the person of the analyst or his friends. His relationship with women changed as well as his choice of girl friends. He no longer sought women in order "to jump into their skin and see through their eyes," that is, to acquire their femaleness, but as he now described it, "I use women to express my femaleness"; that is, he projected onto them those aspects of himself which he now disliked and from which he was trying to free himself, namely, those aspects which he identified with the weak and passive girl. It should be mentioned that the patient was able to accept termination of analysis in a little over a year after the operation with a great deal of equanimity, without any physical symptoms and without any disruption of his life. He continued to make progres after discharge.

The striking aftermath of the phase of analysis climaxed by the abandonment of his stomach thus was the development of the patient's ability to make continual progress toward discarding the original inverted image of himself with which he appears to have begun life and in which he had become fixated.

CONCLUSION AND SUMMARY

It was not my intention to discuss this case in all its complexities but rather to present material that illustrates and validates the concept of the conversion process put forward by Felix Deutsch in the Workshop and in this volume. The course of development of the patient after giving up his stomach at the stage in analysis in which it occurred, I feel, gives full support to the concepts formulated here regarding the effect which the loss of visual sensory perception had on the body image and on the conversion processes and symptoms in the gastrointestinal tract. Vision was impaired not only as a result of organic damage, but the impairment was greatly increased by the nature of the conversion processes and symptoms in the eyes. The eyes had become inverted in their symbolic representations due to the introjection of orally organized and passive feminine figures and parts of them into the eyes, and due to the loss of phallic representation in them. This served to channel symbolic processes into the gastrointestinal tract to the extent that it was as if he were all mouth, all cavity, which the patient equated with the completely passive and feminine woman.

The patient himself expressed his unconscious awareness of this in many ways, especially when he said "If I were to get vision by an operation I'd have no ulcer. If I were to be blind, the world closes down and I run to security." As a result of the changes in the eyes, organic and psychological, he became fixated on an oral symbiotic level. It was the impairment of eye function in the sense described here that made his symbolized functions of the body so concrete. To quote the patient, "With my eyes closed my fantasies are real." He thus was deprived of adequate means to establish his own identity clearly.

The gastrointestinal tract, as a result, had become inextricably bound up with representations of all members of his family, especially his mother. The amalgamation of symbolic processes with basic physiological functions in the gastro-intestinal tract had become so profound that it raised the question continually as to whether the patient would ever be able to free himself from his immobilization in a regressive symbiotic state without his having to express the disentangle-ment of these two sets of processes in the concrete terms of giving up his stomach. The patient continually predicted that such an event would be inevitable if ever he were to find his way out of his difficulties. The concept of the conversion process as formulated by Felix Deutsch can elucidate the unconscious sources of the patient's conviction and the rea-sons for its fulfillment.

13.

DISCUSSION

HENRY M. FOX:

The psychoanalytic concept of conversion, as summarized by Fenichel (1945), refers to symptomatic changes in physical functions which unconsciously and in a distorted form give expression to instinctual impulses that had previously been repressed. The participants in this workshop have emphasized conversion as an *active process* and have regarded symptoms as the end result. Several of the papers illustrate the function of the conversion process as a regressive defense which modifies the patient's own body image as a substitute for a more realistic adaptation to the external world. Dr. Deutsch describes this in terms of the cathexis of external objects followed by a *retrojection* onto the body. The process may involve genital or pregenital symbolization and several of the papers have illustrated associated physiological alterations. Dr. Deutsch has regarded the *threshold* of sensorimotor perceptivity as the central source for the development of the conversion symptoms. Thus the disturbance in ego function which maintains the process of conversion particularly affects the quality of symbolization and perception.

When Freud was discovering the psychoanalytic method through the study of hysterical conversion, he was also attempting to establish the basis for a general psychology. His earliest conception of the ego defined it as an organization with a constant "sum of excitation." In the language of physiology it was described as a group of neurones and when Freud gave up the attempt to explain psychology in terms of brain physiology, the ego was characterized as a group of ideas. As Hartmann (1956) has pointed out, however, the idea of an ego characterized by its *functions* and its relation to the external world and to other mental processes was described by Freud with the greatest definiteness in his "Project for a Scientific Psychology" as early as 1895.

The reconsideration of the conversion process in the light of the most recent psychoanalytic concepts concerning ego function as well as the latest development in brain physiology, endocrinology, and biochemistry encourage the hope that *methods* may now be developed for the observation of a wide range of psychophysiological phenomena. Freud did not, of course, publish the "Project for a Scientific Psychology" and apparently recognized the futility of his attempt to transcribe the phenomena of psychology into the language of physiology and physics current at that time. Nevertheless, as Ernest Jones (1953) remarked, Freud believed much more strongly in his early years, but perhaps to some extent always, that the correlation of mental processes with physiological ones hinted at a similarity in the way both worked.

Symbolization, perception, and the maintenance of quantitative balances can all be studied as expressions of biological adaptation, by psychological and also by physiological *methods*. In a lecture on "Symbolic Mechanisms in Biology," A. K. McIntyre, a neurophysiologist, recently reminded us that "the complex and inextricably intermingled processes of perception, mental activity, and motor performance all depend on symbolic processes. One's appreciation of the external world and awareness of self depend not only on the play of physical and chemical influences (stimuli) upon the sense organs, but upon their conversion into and symbolic representations by incredibly complex pathways of quite different physiochemical events within the nervous system, symbols of which as such we have no direct awareness. It is this dynamic play of symbols in specific spatial and temporal patterns within the cerebral cortex that creates the perceptual world of each individual, a world that is not the same as the outside 'physical world' from which the external stimuli take origin." Relevant neurophysiological *methods* include microscopic studies of nerve conduction, e.g., or electroencephalography.

In a Maudsley lecture delivered in 1933, Adolf Meyer referred to symbolization as the characteristic psychobiological function that we call mentation or "a mind" in varying degrees of overt performance. Freud's revolutionary contribution to psychology, as Jones suggests, was perhaps not so much his demonstrating the existence of an unconscious, and perhaps not even his exploration of its content, as his proposition that there are two fundamentally different kinds of mental processes, which he termed primary and secondary respectively, together with his description of them. Conversion, of course, richly illustrates displacement, condensation, reversal, and other features characteristic of symbolization according to the primary process.

Right from the beginning of his work Freud regarded perception as an active and not merely a passive process. The fact that the nature of an individual's perception expresses the dynamic pattern of his drives and his defenses provides the basis for projective studies of personality such as the Rorschach as well as explaining shifts in sensory emphasis and inhibition illustrated by Dr. Deutsch and the contributions of the other authors in this volume. All of these contributions were based, of course, on the psychoanalytic method of observation.

Quantitative balances can, like symbolization and perception, be studied by physiological as well as by psychological methods. Walter Cannon originally suggested the term homeostasis to designate "the coordinated physiological processes which maintain most of the steady states in the organism." Cannon added that "the word does not imply

something set and immobile, a stagnation. It means a condition—a condition which may vary but which is relatively constant." Physiological methods include, e.g., the measurement
of the excretion levels of steroids and other substances which
indicate the state of pituitary-adrenal or pituitary-ovarian
balances. Such methods require evaluation of the limits of
error in any technique used for measurement and the findings can be compared to the standard deviation for the series
of observations under consideration. Psychoanalytic methods
for the study of quantitative balances depend on the application of Freud's principle of constancy which he enunciated as
early as 1894. Hartmann (1956) has recently commented that
in the structural phase of his theories Freud emphasized the
biological function of the ego more definitely than in his
earlier writings and that by the time he wrote the *Outline*
(1939), he even described self-preservation as an ego function.
The organizing activity of the ego, Hartmann agrees, has
rightly been compared with Cannon's concept of homeostasis
or described as one level of it.

The reconsideration of the theory of the conversion process
and the illustration of these concepts by clinical material has
made a significant contribution to psychophysiology and to
our understanding of the relationship of mind and body. It
seems relevant, however, to remind ourselves that the body is
part of external reality with external relations of its own as
well as contributing sensations to the formation of the body
image. Peripheral body organs are mentally integrated to
only a limited extent and it would therefore be misleading,
e.g., to attribute the sole *cause* of any physical disease to
alterations in perception and symbolization.

Although changes in the body image may be reflected in
far-reaching physiological alterations, this can only be effected
through the agency of the central nervous system via neuroendocrine pathways which are still to a large extent unexplored. Suggestive correlations, for instance, between the

regressive dynamic balances resulting from disturbances in the function of the ego with associated alterations in the neuroendocrine environment of tissues which became cancerous were indicated by some of the clinical observations reported in the papers we have just heard. A clear appreciation of the limitations imposed by our ignorance, however, concerning the relationship of mind and brain as well as recognition of our incomplete understanding of the physiological connections between the central nervous system and the humoral balances of the body will avoid misleading conclusions. Further investigation of symbolization, perception, and the maintenance of quantitative balances by physiological and by psychological methods *within their respective framework of observation* seem to provide the best opportunity gradually to establish the highly significant psychophysiological correlations suggested by the reports of the participants in this panel.

AVERY WEISMAN:

Many people have taken issue with the phrase, "mysterious leap from mind to body," as if it implied a duality in organic life. But Dr. Deutsch's concept of the "psychosomatic" unit long ago indicated that no leap is necessary, for between the psychic and somatic there is no absolute distinction—there is only psychological language and physiological language. "Somatic" refers to the observable features of the object of perception, while "psychic" pertains to the experiential features of the subject who perceives. The major difficulty occurs in comprehending the processes which go on in the mysterious internuncial region between perception and behavior and between fantasy and function—an area which neither psychoanalysis nor neurophysiology has yet penetrated.

There are many ambiguities in the terms, retrojection, symbolization, and conversion, which must be clarified before the full significance of this contribution may be satisfactorily evaluated. For example, retrojection suffers from being a relatively new word by which to characterize a not unfamiliar process. Moreover, symbolization has been used in so many ways by workers in psychology, linguistics, and philosophy that it is difficult to restrict it to the special sense of this discussion. It is not clear whether symbolization refers to the process by which perceptual organs receive cathexis, to the means of retaining lost objects by representing their common features in repressed memory, or to a phase of reality testing which uses both percepts and concepts. I believe that "symbolization" has distinct meanings which depend on whether or not one speaks in the topographical, economic, or dynamic idiom. The theory of the conversion process is so comprehensive, therefore, that it may be in danger of meaning all things to all men. It may then lose some of the exquisite precision with which certain aspects may be clinically verified.

The theory of the conversion process is based on three general formulations: (1) perceptions alter subsequent perceptions by modifying the organ of perception; (2) lost objects are restored by retrojection of new sensory objects; and (3) by symbolization, are recreated and preserved in the unconscious, together with repressed perceptions of great emotional significance but lowered sensory threshold. These formulations are admittedly oversimplified to the point of distortion, for clearly it is not the literal eye which is changed by the sight of the beloved, nor is the tongue modified by each successive taste sensation. It is the interpretation of the perception which alters subsequent acts of perception. When a lover catches sight of his beloved, the eye, retina, optic nerves and occipital lobes are not structurally altered, but the erotic fantasies evoked by the perception modify the entire motivated act of sight. The visual apparatus participates in the act, but it does not motivate the act.

According to the theory, the conversion process is constantly in action and has universal application. How then can pathological conversion states be explained? Repression, too, occurs in everyone, but patients are called hysterical when repression is unduly active and when there is increased fantasy formation and heightened identification with the objects of fantasy. The development of pathological conversion symptoms seems to depend as much on the kind of fantasy which is repressed as upon the processes of conversion, symbolization, and retrojection. I suggest that these functions require a special kind of material before clinical conversion symptoms may develop, and that the function of repression of certain parts of the content is of crucial importance. If there is a specific fantasy of a motivated act which has been repressed and symbolized, certain unmotivated visceral and somatic functions which participate in the performance of the act may be altered. As a result, all that reaches consciousness may be in the form of perceptions which reflect hyperfunction or hypofunction of these functions. Although only the latter may present themselves as clinical symptoms, it is the total motivated act rather than its individual components which are disturbed. In this way, conversion may be both normal and pathological. If conversion deals only with lost objects, then no abnormalities arise. But when fantasies are caught up in conflict of opposing psychic acts, then organic recollections may evoke pathological consequences of the normal conversion process.

This brief discussion cannot close without recognizing that the concept of the psychosomatic unit, synesthesia, and unity of the body image with the psychic has raised such basic questions that it will require many generations before these issues can be resolved. It is admittedly not simple, but neither is it an intellectual *cul de sac*.

PHILLIP H. GATES:

In this symposium it becomes almost too obvious to comment that the concept of conversion as it was originally formulated to explain certain of the phenomena of hysteria needs to be thought of as a mechanism used defensively by a wide variety of patients with differing presenting problems. The authors of the papers have amply illustrated this. Historically, most notable has been the progression from the rather general conception of the transformation of an excitation (Freud, 1893) to the transformation of libido into anxiety, the accompanying fantasy being repressed and then manifested in a symptom (Freud, 1894), and the more recent views that the vicissitudes of aggression must be accounted for in order to give a more satisfying explanation of particular symptom formations, e.g., colitis. An awareness that certain transformations of drives were more simple or more primitive than others, for example, vomiting, has been noted previously as in Alexander's distinction of somatic reactions on the basis of voluntary on the one hand and involuntary or vegetative innervation on the other, and in Fenichel's concept of pregenital conversion. The precise mechanisms involved, however, have not been explained as clearly as seems desirable.

It is proposed in this note that the distinction of whether primary process or secondary process predominates in the formation of particular symptoms would assist in clarifying the explanation of any specific clinical example. To illustrate this the following model is suggested. A five-year-old boy is attacked from the rear by his seven-year-old brother. The younger boy is knocked to the floor, sprawling on his face while making futile efforts to protect himself, and in so doing, defecates in his pants. Assuming that the younger boy had reached the utilization of secondary process in many aspects of ego function, under the impact of the combined anxiety and anger stimulated by the older brother, the younger one reverted to a somatic (organ) expression that can be regarded as primary process, but in which aggression has undergone a transformation from expression via the muscular system to expression by means of a system and organ that are known to have both libidinal and aggressive connotations as well as excretory function. Furthermore, it is an affective discharge that may be assumed to have been determined as to selection of mode of discharge by previous experience in the course of bowel training. It appears necessary, however, to consider more fully the direction of the aggression.

Here we may profitably follow the thinking of Hartmann, Kris, and Loewenstein (1949) as to whether "acts of actual or 'true' self-destruction occur, or whether the observed destructive actions of the infant—such as self-infliction of damage, f.i., by scratching—can be explained by assuming that the distinction between self and external world is not yet possible, and that unpleasure or pain are not yet recognized as signals of danger, because of the incomplete awareness of the bodily self as represented in the image of the body." For a model we may take a four-and-a-half-year-old boy observed and treated for an extended period of time at the James Jackson Putnam Children's Center. In a situation of being deprived by a little girl in the nursery school of his being able to complete a play action, he made only an abortive attempt to regain the lost play object, then gave up the effort, yelled, cried, threw himself to the floor, scratched and clawed violently with his fingernails at his eyes, wrists, and genital, verbalized the wish and attempted the action of throwing himself out the window. In this instance there is direct evidence of his having been threatened with spanking on the genital by his nurse, and it is not beyond reasonable supposition that the eyes had been the site of pain during washing with soap, and that his wrists had been restrained in a variety of situations including reproofs for attacks on his younger sister. Here again secondary process in the ego had shown some manifestations in the fantasy he was playing out at the time of the frustration, but the aggression that was provoked was of such a degree that the frail ego disintegrated under the impact of the anxiety arising from his wish to retaliate in accordance with his memories. It may be surmised that there had occurred previously identifications with the aggressive actions to which he had been forced to submit, identifications that were linked to memories of painful perceptions both tactile and visual, and that in the state of ego disintegration, his ego was not able to make the reality distinctions between his own self and the self of the depriving object. That is, the ego could not distinguish between the site of the peripheral end organs of perception and the central perceptions that would include an awareness on the one hand of the image of his own body and of his personal self and on the other hand of the image of the frustrating object. The transformation of the aggressive drive into the kind of internal direction that has been described in this brief illustration with the specific elements that determine the body parts that are used in the discharge of the aggression would tend first to confirm the hypothesis that the aggressive drive must be accorded similar vicissitudes to those denoted to the libidinal drives in the process of conversion, and further that the state of self-differentiation and the state of ego organization with particular respect to the capacity to maintain functioning of the secondary process would need to be taken into account in explaining clinical phenomena.

SANFORD GIFFORD:

Two general impressions of Dr. Deutsch's theory of the conversion process are striking, its empirical effect on the members of the Workshop, in stimulating a remarkable series of papers, and its sweeping theoretical implications, in understanding normal mechanisms of psychophysiological regulation as well as the psychopathology and taxonomy of psychosomatic disorders. First, each author interpreted the conversion process somewhat differently, making use of it ac-

cording to his own special interests and finding original clinical applications in a variety of different areas, but the concept itself performed the function of a fruitful organizing
principle, both unifying and permitting diversity. Second,
Dr. Deutsch has extended the conventional concept of conversion to include almost every phenomenon in which an
interrelationship exists between psychic processes and bodily
representations. It may be asked whether this new usage is
necessary, since every scientist, in an age of terminological
proliferation, must first question the introduction of new
terms and the modification of old reliable ones. After some
initial reservations, I believe that Dr. Deutsch's innovation
is necessary, because no existing term is comprehensive
enough to include normal psychophysiological processes,
transient sensorimotor phenomena of everyday life, specific
changes in body representations during psychoanalysis, the
classical conversion symptoms of hysteria and severe psychosomatic disorders.

It is interesting that Dr. Deutsch formulated his concept
of the conversion process in his paper of 1924, but that his
interests led him to explore many other aspects of the mind-
body problem before returning to it at the present time.
Perhaps in those pioneer days, when a unitary theory of mind
and body was gradually being established, a taxonomy of
psychosomatic disease was more urgently required than an
all-inclusive synthesis, as in the early development of many
sciences. Otto Fenichel (1945) made important contributions
to this problem, in his comprehensive classification of conversion symptoms, affect equivalents, and organ neuroses. He
extended Alexander's (1943) differentiation between conversions, as symbolic representations of conflicts expressed in
the voluntary musculature, and organ neuroses, as conflicts
affecting the autonomic innervation of smooth muscle, with
his concept of "the disturbed chemistry of the unsatisfied
person." Fenichel was well aware of the limitations of this

nomenclature, however, pointing out how many symptoms involved both smooth and striated muscle and introducing the concept of "pregenital conversions" to increase the flexibility of his classification. Many recent advances in psychosomatic research show a progressive tendency toward unifying principles, emphasizing the difficulties of defining organ-specific or conflict-specific clinical entities, regarding all psychosomatic disorders as widespread disturbances in psychophysiological integration, and recognizing that the ego structure of patients with these disorders is closer to the psychoses than the neuroses. The time may have arrived for a comprehensive theory like Dr. Deutsch's that includes both normal and pathological phenomena, regardless of whether "conversion process" or some other term is eventually established in common usage.

Rather than commenting on individual papers, I would like to discuss the general concept of the conversion process, and to add some remarks about its contribution to the phenomena of everyday life. On first acquaintance, Dr. Deutsch's theory presents certain difficulties, partly because several conventional terms are used in a new or unusual sense. For this reason, I will begin by offering my own understanding of the concept, even at the risk of some repetition. It has already been stressed that Dr. Deutsch has enlarged the term "conversion," from its meaning in Freud's early writings, as the transformation of repressed libido into a bodily symptom that symbolizes an instinctual conflict, to the general concept of a normal psychophysiological process that operates continuously throughout the life of the individual and results in pathological symptom formation only when it undergoes fixation through some specific physical or emotional disturbance.

The first occurrence of the conversion process, as I understand it, can be recognized in the hallucinatory wish fulfillment of the newborn infant, which Dr. Deutsch calls "projection onto the outer world," in a different sense from projection as a delusional phenomenon. In the undifferentiated state of the first weeks of life, the infant cannot distinguish between himself, his own body parts, contact with his mother and his rudimentary perceptions of external reality. Differentiation between himself and the outer world takes place through a succession of periodic losses, when the absence of his mother's comforting is experienced as losing a part of himself and this loss is temporarily restored by hallucinating the object that provides gratification. If I comprehend Dr. Deutsch's concept correctly, the infant associates each experience of loss and gratification, as well as the physiochemical substrate of these experiences, with certain primitive perceptions of his body, his environment, and the earliest external objects. These perceptions include enteroceptive sensations from viscera, the erogenous zones, the movement of bodily parts and position in space, the exteroceptive sensations of pain, touch, temperature, and rudimentary distance perceptions of hearing, smell, and vision. Repeated experiences of deprivation and gratification gradually establish a characteristic psychophysiological Gestalt, in which a biochemical state of anabolism or catabolism, an affect of pleasure or unpleasure, and a configuration of sense perceptions from the body and from the outer world are associated with the loss or restitution of the earliest precursors of object relations. The manner in which this psychophysiological Gestalt comes to represent the original object, subsequently differentiated as the infant's mother, is the process that Dr. Deutsch calls "symbolization." His term "retrojection" indicates the re-creation of this psychophysiological configuration following later experiences of object loss, when the integrity of the ego is restored, sometimes in a pathological form, by the reincorporation of the lost object in fantasies, bodily symptoms or pathophysiological changes.

The unique character of each conversion process, for every

individual and for different periods in his life, is the outcome of many complex factors: genetic or constitutional features of drive endowment, innate ego variations in the capacity to tolerate deprivation, constitutional tendencies toward stability or lability of homeostatic regulation, the vicissitudes of early object relations, and the timing and pattern of emotional losses in later childhood. Presumably certain conversion processes are established early, while others are continuously laid down throughout life. They may remain latent indefinitely, until a life experience recapitulates the original object loss, or a mental or physical event reduplicates some aspect of the original psychophysiological Gestalt and reactivates the entire complex. Many contributions to the psychosomatic literature have established the well-known occurrence of psychosomatic disorders after a significant object loss or narcissistic injury, when the conversion process may manifest itself in severe pathophysiological regression and eventually in structural bodily changes. Dr. Deutsch's previous work has outlined, in exquisite microanalytic detail, the occurrence of transient, reversible conversion processes during psychoanalysis, when the vicissitudes of early object relations are recapitulated in the transference neurosis and associated with characteristic patterns of affect, body movement and sensation, and altered awareness of external perceptual stimuli. I will add a few examples from everyday life to illustrate the ubiquitous nature of the conversion process.

When a habitual smoker sits down to prepare a scientific discussion, a fleeting sense of helplessness leads to an indefinable somatic sensation, vaguely referred to the region of the mouth, and a quasi-automatic movement of the hand toward a source of tobacco. When the need is gratified, this conversion process, which reflects primitive oral cravings, may scarcely reach the threshold of consciousness. When the smoker is deprived of tobacco, however, there are disturbances in affect, perception, motility, and reality testing that seem to represent the primitive psychophysiological Gestalt associated with early object loss. The localization and quality of these experiences is varied and characteristic for the individual. In one person a strange sensation is referred to the back of the throat, associated with swallowing and a tight feeling in the breast; in another the altered body awareness is vaguely localized in the forepart of the mouth and tongue, or deep in the chest and associated with respiration. Diffuse motor restlessness and hyperactivity may occur, and there are specific sensations and semi-involuntary movements in the hands. Disturbances in the perception of external stimuli range from hyperacuity to sensory distortions and feelings of unreality and depersonalization. Characteristic of all these experiences is the vague, indefinable quality of the bodily sensations, intense but difficult to localize, and the association with motor disturbances and an affect of unpleasure. These characteristics resemble Spitz's concept (1955) of the infant's early nursing experience, in which sensations in the hands, organs of equilibrium and skin, later merged with the first visual percepts, "combine with the intraoral sensations to [create] a unified situational experience in which no part is distinguishable from the other."

The opposite kind of experience, in which a specific combination of sense perceptions revives the affects associated with early object losses is well-known in literature. The most famous example is Proust's recollection of his mother putting him to bed, evoked by the association of a special cake dipped in tea. He also describes a vivid sequence of past experiences that were recalled by the proprioceptive sensations of walking on an uneven pavement with each foot on a different level. A more specific example is described by an internist* who gave an injection of epinephrine to a phobic woman. Although not anxious at the time, the physiological sensations

* Dr. I. Herbert Scheinberg, personal communication.

usually associated with her fears compelled her to run to the window, as if to reassure herself that her children were unharmed.

One last remark about the contribution that the conversion process makes to the psychoanalytic concept of restitution after object loss. The concept of "psychophysiological regression" has recently been criticized (Mendelson, Hirsch, and Webber, 1956) on the naïve grounds that psychosomatic disorders are not precise reduplications of infantile physiological states. Dr. Deutsch's theory of the conversion process makes it possible to understand these disorders as the complex outcome of both regression and restitution, as in the psychoses. It is obvious that schizophrenic thought disorders are not literal reproductions of infantile modes of communication but disturbances at many levels of functioning, with the preservation of some higher functions, regressions in certain areas, and attempts at re-establishing emotional contact. Something similar may be said about ulcerative colitis, for example, which does not reproduce infantile patterns of bowel functioning but constitutes a widespread disturbance in many areas of ego functioning and homeostatic regulation. There are difficulties in eating and sleeping, headache, fever, general overactivity or inertia, and sometimes skin and joint lesions, as well as bleeding and inflammation of the bowel. It is possible that some of these symptoms represent distorted attempts at healing and reparation, just as the over-all aim of the conversion process is psychophysiological restitution, to restore the lost object and to re-establish instinctual and biochemical equilibrium.

PETER H. KNAPP:

Dr. Deutsch, it seems to me, has attempted to extend conceptually the scope of the process called "conversion." First, he has conjectured as to its origins in time, in the primitive experience of loss and infantile reactions of compensation.

Secondly, he has extended it, if you like, in space, proposing that much of life is repetition of this early pattern, symbolically disguised.

One cannot fail to be impressed by Dr. Deutsch's new concept. It may need further corroboration, perhaps even conceptual clarification, but the avenues which it opens are many. In particular, of course, it contributes to the psychosomatic field. More than anyone writing in this area, he appears to me to have grasped some of the principles which truly unify it. Explicitly, he starts his symposium with Freud's question: how to account for "mysterious leap from mind to the body." He shows how in infancy the organism's "attention," "energy," or "cathexis"—the term one chooses is not crucial—may be channelized, in response to infantile needs, and that the constellations so established may evolve toward a characteristic functional representation later in life. Both "body" and "mind" are traced back to their indisputable oneness in the infant. Implicitly, he thus supports the view, which I share with others of the discussants, that the "leap" is merely from one adult point of view to another.

The papers of Dr. Deutsch's co-workers consist largely of clinical applications of this approach. Drs. Silverman, Menzer-Benaron, Mann, Mushatt, and the other collaborators with Dr. Deutsch have applied his broad conceptualization of the conversion process to many areas, not only those of autonomic nervous and endocrine dysfunction—the traditional "psychosomatic" disorders—but those of major mental derangement and even malignant disease. This is a bold effort, made easier by the reduced need to think of separate "mental" and "physical" events interacting across some cosmic gap. It can, of course, lead to speculative dangers of its own. The authors, I am sure, recognize the preliminary nature of their explorations. Obviously much remains to be done. The bold point of view and the fruitful generalization must be worked out with thoroughness, using the refinements of research method now available, and paying due heed to those aspects of disease processes which can be observed, described, even measured in biologic terms.

One additional problem is suggested by these papers, that of differentiating individuals, one from the other. Assuming Dr. Deutsch's broad application of the conversion concept to be valid, we still are left with the question of choice of neurosis. With this, psychoanalysis has made little progress. It is much stronger, as several of our colleagues in the social sciences have pointed out, as a psychology which illuminates processes, than one which separates out entities. We still have little knowledge of why the conversion process should predominate in certain persons, much less why it should lead to involvement of one area, or to one type of lesion, rather than another. The question seems particularly pertinent in this symposium, since Freud, after all, started out more than half a century ago to find "the cause" of hysteria. The results of his search were monumental. Today we might phrase the question differently. But the quest is still ours.

FELIX DEUTSCH:

In conclusion, I would like to emphasize that these clinical contributions to the problem of the conversion theory collected in this volume by no means close the chapter of "the mysterious leap from the mind to the body." They were designed to stimulate further investigations of this problem, based on the formula: projection—loss—symbolization—retrojection and re-embodiment. This concept envisages the pathways which lead through the thoroughfare of conversion, recognizing the conversion process as the perpetual life stream which is kept flowing by the fountains of symbolization. Their earliest seeds are growing out of the primary processes.

Of course, several other channels lead also into this stream. They were dealt with in the framework of this monograph.

By and large, the embodiment of the symbols can be called the "soul" of the organism. Without them, psychic life expires. Therefore, this concept of conversion as a continually active process normally innate in the organism serves as the basis for the assumption that this process plays a part in any normal and neurotic condition.

May I add some further remarks which express a look into the future. I am of the opinion that in the future this postulate may replace the concept of "psychogenesis" and might even substitute the term "psychosomatic." As far as the term "psychogenesis" is concerned, I had called it outmoded fifteen years ago.

"There does not exist," I wrote, "the alternative of psychogenic or not psychogenic." The fundamental question is: what is the interrelationship of certain psychological factors with certain biological ones? To make it clear: not coexistence, nor corollary, or correlation, nor parallelism of psychological factors, but *interrelationship* of these factors is what we will find. More specifically, we have to search for the roots of the *interaction* of the emotional life and the related bodily functions, *what* led to the choice of the organic system for the expression of the conflict, and furthermore, what factors of the environment, past and present, contributed to the establishment of the psychosomatic symptom complex.

More difficult will be the substitution of the term psychosomatic by a new one covering its present meaning. The term is already inveterated, although when I used it in analysis the first time thirty-two years ago, I was quite aware of the ambiguity hidden in this word. Hence to use an all-inclusive term of "conversion," it will require specific data on the type, level and degree of the conversion process involved. It will call for more research before such a new comprehensive terminology can be introduced.

The papers of this workshop are a beginning in this direction.

BIBLIOGRAPHY

Alexander, Franz (1939), Emotional Factors in Essential Hypertension. *Psychosom. Med.*, 1:173-179.

—— (1943), Fundamental Concepts of Psychosomatic Research. *Psychosom. Med.*, 5:205-210.

—— (1950), *Studies in Psychosomatic Medicine.* New York: Norton.

Bacon, Catherine L. (1954), Psychosomatic Observations in Cardiac Pain. *Psa. Quart.*, 23:7-19.

—— (1956), The Role of Aggression in the Asthmatic Attack. *Psa. Quart.*, 25:309-324.

—— & Renneker, Richard; Cutler, Max (1952), A Psychosomatic Study of Cancer of the Breast. *Psychosom. Med.*, 14:453-460.

Bak, Robert C. (1939), Regression of Ego-Orientation and Libido in Schizophrenia. *Int. J. Psa.*, 20:1-8.

—— (1946), Masochism in Paranoia. *Psa. Quart.*, 15:285.

—— (1954), The Schizophrenic Defense against Aggression. *Int. J. Psa.*, 35:129-134.

Benedek, Therese (1952), *Psychosexual Functions in Women.* New York: Ronald Press.

Bernstein, I. (1957), The Role of Narcissism in Moral Masochism. *Psa. Quart.*, 26:358.

Bibring, Edward (1941), The Development and Problems of the Theory of the Instincts. *Int. J. Psa.*, 22:102-131.

Bion, W. R. (1954), Notes on the Theory of Schizophrenia. *Int. J. Psa.*, 35:113-118.

Bower, W. H. & Altschule, M. (1956), Post-Partum Psychosis. *New Engl. J. Med.*, 254:157-160.

Brain, Sir Russell (1950), In: *Physical Basis of Mind,* ed. P. Laslett. Oxford: Oxford University Press.

Breuer, Josef & Freud, Sigmund (1895), Studies on Hysteria. *Standard Edition of the Complete Psychological Works of Sigmund Freud,* Vol. II. London: Hogarth Press, 1955.

Bychowski, Gustav (1945), The Ego of Homosexuals. *Int. J. Psa.*, 26:114-127.

255

—— (1952), *Psychotherapy of Psychotics.* New York: Grune & Stratton.

Cannon, Walter B. (1934), *Bodily Changes in Pain, Hunger, Fear and Rage.* New York: Appleton-Century.

Cobb, Stanley (1943), *Borderlands of Psychiatry.* Cambridge: Harvard University Press.

—— (1957), Monism and Psychosomatic Medicine. *Psychosom. Med.,* 19:77.

Cohen, Sir Henry (1952), Monism. *Philosophy,* 21:1, 1952.

Cremerius, J. (1957), Freud's Concept of the Origin of Psychogenic Bodily Symptoms. *Psyche* (Heidelberg), 11:125.

Deutsch, Felix (1924), Zur Bildung des Konversionssymptoms. *Int. Ztschr. Psa.,* 10:380-392.

—— (1939), The Production of Somatic Disease by Emotional Disturbance. In: *The Interrelationship of Body and Mind.* Baltimore: Williams & Wilkins.

—— (1940), Social Service and Psychosomatic Disease. *Newsletter, Am. Assn. Med. Soc. Workers,* 11:1-9.

—— (1946), Psychosomatic Aspects of Dermatology. *Nerv. Child,* 5:339-364.

—— (1948), The Psychosomatic Concept. *Bull. Johns Hopkins Hosp.,* 80; also in *Acta Med. Orient.,* 7:33-42.

—— (1951), Thus Speaks the Body: Some Psychosomatic Aspects of the Respiratory Disorder Asthma. *Acta Med. Orient.,* 10:67-86.

—— (1954), Analytic Synesthesiology. *Int. J. Psa.,* 35:293-301.

—— (1955), Minutes of the Workshop on the Theory of the Conversion Process. Boston Psychoanalytic Society and Institute.

—— (1956), The Riddle of the Mind-Body Correlations. *Acta Med. Orient.,* 15:167.

—— & Murphy, William F. (1955), *The Clinical Interview,* 2 Vols. New York: International Universities Press.

Deutsch, Helene (1944), *The Psychology of Women,* Vol. I. New York: Grune & Stratton.

Duncan, C. H. & Stevenson, I. P. (1950), Paroxysmal Arrhythmias. *Geriatrics,* 5:259-267.

Eissler, K. R. (1951), Remarks on the Psycho-Analysis of Schizophrenia. *Int. J. Psa.,* 32:139-156.

Fenichel, Otto (1943), The Psychopathology of Coughing. *Psychosom. Med.,* 5:181-184.

—— (1945), *The Psychoanalytic Theory of Neurosis.* New York: Norton.

Ferenczi, Sandor (1914), The Nosology of Male Homosexuality (Homoerotism). *Sex in Psychoanalysis.* New York: Basic Books, 1950.

—— (1916-1917), Pollution without Dream Orgasm and Dream Orgasm without Pollution. *Further Contributions to the Theory and Technique of Psycho-Analysis.* London: Hogarth Press, 1926.

——— (1919), The Phenomena of Hysterical Materialization. *Further Contributions to the Theory and Technique of Psycho-Analysis.* London: Hogarth Press, 1926.

Fisher, Charles (1954), Dreams and Perception: The Role of Preconscious and Primary Modes of Perception in Dream Formation. *J. Am. Psa. Assn.,* 2:389-445.

Fox, Henry M. (1953), Psychological Responses to ACTH and Cortisone. *Psychosom. Med.,* 15:614-627.

——— (1958), Effect of Psychophysiological Research on the Transference. *J. Am. Psa. Assn.,* 6:413-432.

——— et al. (1957), Some Methods of Observing Humans under Stress. *Psychiat. Research Report,* No. 7, Am. Psychiat. Assn.

——— (1958), Urinary 17-Hydroxycorticoids and Uropepsin Levels with Psychological Data. *Arch. Int. Med.,* 101:859-871.

French, Thomas M. & Alexander, Franz; Bacon, Catherine L.; et al. (1941), Psychogenic Factors in Bronchial Asthma. *Psychosom. Med. Mon.,* No. 4 (Washington).

Anna Freud (1936), *The Ego and the Mechanisms of Defense.* New York: International Universities Press, 1936.

——— (1952), The Role of Bodily Illness in the Mental Life of Children. *The Psychoanalytic Study of the Child,* 7:69-81. New York: International Universities Press.

Freud, Sigmund (1887-1902), *The Origins of Psychoanalysis. Letters, Drafts and Notes to Wilhelm Fliess (1887-1902).* New York: Basic Books, 1954.

——— (1891), *On Aphasia.* New York: International Universities Press, 1953.

——— (1892), A Letter to Josef Breuer. *Collected Papers,* 5:25. London: Hogarth Press, 1950.

——— (1893), On the Psychical Mechanism of Hysterical Phenomena. *Collected Papers,* 1:24-41. London: Hogarth Press, 1924.

——— (1894), The Defence Neuro-Psychoses. *Collected Papers,* 1:59-75. London: Hogarth Press, 1924.

——— (1895), Project for a Scientific Psychology. In: Freud (1887-1902).

——— (1896), Further Remarks on the Defence Neuro-Psychoses. *Collected Papers,* 1:155-182. London: Hogarth Press, 1924.

——— (1900), The Interpretation of Dreams. *Standard Edition,* Vols. III & IV. London: Hogarth Press, 1953.

——— (1904), Freud's Psycho-Analytic Procedure. *Standard Edition,* 7:249-256. London: Hogarth Press, 1953.

——— (1905a), Three Essays on the Theory of Sexuality. *Standard Edition,* 7:125-243. London: Hogarth Press, 1953.

———— (1905b), Fragment of an Analysis of a Case of Hysteria. *Standard Edition*, 7:3-122. London: Hogarth Press, 1953.

———— (1908a), Hysterical Phantasies and Their Relation to Bisexuality. *Collected Papers*, 2:51-58. London: Hogarth Press, 1924.

———— (1908b), Character and Anal Erotism. *Collected Papers*, 2:45-50. London: Hogarth Press, 1924.

———— (1909a), Notes upon a Case of Obsessional Neurosis. *Standard Edition*, 10:153-250. London: Hogarth Press, 1955.

———— (1909b), Five Lectures on Psycho-Analysis. *Standard Edition*, 11:3-55. London: Hogarth Press, 1957.

———— (1909c), Analysis of a Phobia in a Five-Year-Old Boy. *Standard Edition*, 10:5-149. London: Hogarth Press, 1955.

———— (1910), Psychogenic Visual Disturbance according to Psycho-Analytical Conceptions. *Collected Papers*, 2:105-112. London: Hogarth Press, 1924.

———— (1911a), Formulations regarding the Two Principles in Mental Functioning. *Collected Papers*, 4:13-21. London: Hogarth Press, 1925.

———— (1911b), Psycho-Analytic Notes upon an Autobiographical Account of a Case of Paranoia Dementia Paranoides. *Collected Papers*, 3:587-605. London: Hogarth Press, 1925.

———— (1912), Types of Neurotic Nosogenesis. *Collected Papers*, 2:113-121. London: Hogarth Press, 1924.

———— (1913), The Predisposition to Obsessional Neurosis. *Collected Papers*, 2:122-132. London: Hogarth Press, 1924.

———— (1914a), On the History of the Psycho-Analytic Movement. *Standard Edition*, 14:7-66. London: Hogarth Press, 1957.

———— (1914b), On Narcissism: An Introduction. *Standard Edition*, 14:67-102. London: Hogarth Press, 1957.

———— (1914c), Further Recommendations in the Technique of Psycho-Analysis. Recollection, Repetition and Working Through. *Collected Papers*, 2:366-376. London: Hogarth Press, 1924.

———— (1915a), Repression. *Standard Edition*, 14:141-158. London: Hogarth Press, 1957.

———— (1915b), The Unconscious. *Standard Edition*, 14:159-216. London: Hogarth Press, 1957.

———— (1915c), A Case of Paranoia Running Counter to the Psycho-Analytic Theory of the Disease. *Standard Edition*, 14:261-272. London: Hogarth Press, 1957.

———— (1915d), Instincts and Their Vicissitudes. *Standard Edition*, 14:109-140. London: Hogarth Press, 1957.

———— (1916a), Some Character-Types Met with in Psycho-Analytic Work. *Standard Edition*, 14:309-333. London: Hogarth Press, 1957.

———— (1916b), On the Transformation of Instincts with Special Reference to Anal Erotism. *Collected Papers*, 2:164-171. London: Hogarth Press, 1924.

———— (1916-1917), *A General Introduction to Psychoanalysis*. New York: Boni & Liveright, 1920.

———— (1917), Mourning and Melancholia. *Collected Papers*, 4:152-170. London: Hogarth Press, 1925.

———— (1918), From the History of an Infantile Neurosis. *Standard Edition*, 17:7-122. London: Hogarth Press, 1955.

———— (1919), A Child Is Being Beaten. *Collected Papers*, 2:172-201. London: Hogarth Press, 1924.

———— (1920), Beyond the Pleasure Principle. *Standard Edition*, 18:3-64. London: Hogarth Press, 1955.

———— (1923a), A Neurosis of Demoniacal Possession in the Seventeenth Century. *Collected Papers*, 4:436-472. London: Hogarth Press, 1925.

———— (1923b), Two Encyclopaedia Articles. *Collected Papers*, 5:107-135. London: Hogarth Press, 1950.

———— (1923c), *The Ego and the Id*. London: Hogarth Press, 1927.

———— (1923d), Footnote to Postscript of Fragment of an Analysis of a Case of Hysteria. (See Freud, 1905b).

———— (1924a), The Economic Problem in Masochism. *Collected Papers*, 2:255-268. London: Hogarth Press, 1924.

———— (1924b), The Passing of the Oedipus Complex. *Collected Papers*, 2:269-276. London: Hogarth Press, 1924.

———— (1924c), Neurosis and Psychosis. *Collected Papers*, 2:250-254. London: Hogarth Press, 1924.

———— (1924d), The Loss of Reality in Neurosis and Psychosis. *Collected Papers*, 2:255-268. London: Hogarth Press, 1924.

———— (1925), *An Autobiographical Study*. New York: Norton, 1935.

———— (1926), *Inhibition, Symptom and Anxiety*. London: Hogarth Press, 1936.

———— (1932), *New Introductory Lectures on Psychoanalysis*. New York: Norton, 1933.

———— (1937), Analysis Terminable and Interminable. *Collected Papers*, 5:316-357. London: Hogarth Press, 1950.

———— (1938), Some Elementary Lessons in Psycho-Analysis. *Collected Papers*, 5:376-382. London: Hogarth Press, 1950.

———— (1939), *An Outline of Psychoanalysis*. New York: Norton, 1949.

———— & Breuer, J. (1892), On the Theory of Hysterical Attacks. *Collected Papers*, 5:27-32. London: Hogarth Press, 1950.

———— ———— See Breuer & Freud (1895).

Fromm-Reichmann, Frieda (1937), Contribution to the Psychogenesis of Migraine. *Psa. Rev.*, 24:26-33.

—————— (1940), Note on the Mother Role in the Family Group. *Bull. Menninger Clin.*, 4:132-148.

—————— (1946), Remarks on the Philosophy of Mental Disorder. *Psychiatry*, 9:293-308.

Fuller, J. L. & Easler, C.; Smith, M. (1950), Inheritance of Audiogenic Seizure Susceptibility in the Mouse. *Genetics*, 35:622.

Garma, Angel (1957), Oral-Digestive Superego Aggressions and Actual Conflicts in Peptic Ulcer Patients. *Int. J. Psa.*, 38:73-81.

Gates, P. & Weinberger, J. (1955), The Concept of the Damaged Body in Psychosomatic Complaints of the Genitourinary Tract. *Psa. Rev.*, 42:17-23.

Gerard, R. W. (1936), Factors Controlling Brain Potentials. *Cold Spring Harbor Symposia*, No. 4.

Glauber, I. P. (1956), The Rebirth Motif in Homosexuality and Its Teleological Significance. *Int. J. Psa.*, 37:416-421.

Graham, D. T. & Wolf, S. (1950), Pathogenesis of Urticaria. *Psychosom. Med.*, 13:122.

Greenacre, Phyllis (1952), *Trauma, Growth and Personality*. New York: Norton.

Gunther, Lewis & Menninger, Karl A. (1939), Intermittent Extrasystoles Directly Associated with Emotional Conflict. *Bull. Menninger Clin.*, 3:164-176.

Halliday, J. L. (1937), Psychological Factors in Rheumatism. *Brit. J. Med. Psychol.*, 1:213.

Hartmann, Heinz (1950), Comments on the Psychoanalytic Theory of the Ego. *The Psychoanalytic Study of the Child*, 5:74-96. New York: International Universities Press.

—————— (1955), Notes on the Theory of Sublimation. *The Psychoanalytic Study of the Child*, 10:9-29. New York: International Universities Press.

—————— (1956), The Development of the Ego Concept in Freud's Work. *Int. J. Psa.*, 37:425-438.

—————— & Kris, Ernst; Loewenstein, Rudolph M. (1946), Comments on the Formation of Psychic Structure. *The Psychoanalytic Study of the Child*, 2:11-38. New York: International Universities Press.

—————— —————— (1949), Notes on the Theory of Aggression. *The Psychoanalytic Study of the Child*, 3/4:9-36. New York: International Universities Press.

Hayman, Max (1941) Myasthenia Gravis and Psychosis. *Psychosom. Med.*, 3:120-137.

Hebb, D. O. (1957), Psychology as a Biological Science. Address, Harvard University (Feb. 8).

Hendrick, Ives (1931), Ego Defense and the Mechanism of Oral Ejection in Schizophrenia. *Int. J. Psa.*, 12:298-325.

—— (1933), Pregenital Anxiety in a Feminine Passive Character. *Psa. Quart.*, 2: 68-93.

—— (1936), Ego Development and Certain Character Problems. *Psa Quart*, 5:320-346.

—— (1939), The Contributions of Psychoanalysis to the Study of Psychoses. *J. Am. Med. Assn.*, 113:918-924.

—— (1942), Instinct and Ego during Infancy. *Psa. Quart.*, 11:33-58.

Herrick, C. L. (1956), *The Evolution of Human Nature*. Austin: University of Texas Press.

Hoffer, W. (1952), The Mutual Influences in the Development of Ego and Id. *The Psychoanalytic Study of the Child*, 7:31-41. New York: International Universities Press.

Holmes, Thomas H. & Wolff, Harold G. (1950), Life Situations, Emotions and Backache. *Assn. Res. Nerv. & Ment. Dis. Proc.*, 29:750-771.

Hug-Hellmuth, H. (1912), Über Farbenhören. *Imago*, 1:228-264.

Huxley, J. (1953), *Evolution in Action*. New York: Harper.

Isaacs, Susan (1948), The Nature and Function of Phantasy. In: *Developments in Psycho-Analysis*. London: Hogarth Press, 1952.

Jacobson, Edith (1954), On Psychotic Identification. *Int. J. Psa.*, 35:102-108.

James, William (1904), Does Consciousness Exist? In: *Essays in Radical Empiricism*. New York: Longmans Green, 1922, pp. 1-38.

Johnson, Adelaide (1949), Sanctions for Superego Lacunae of Adolescents. In: *Searchlights on Delinquency*, ed. K. R. Eissler. New York: International Universities Press.

Jonas, A. D. (1951), Muscular Dysfunction under Emotional Stress. *Am. Practitioner*, 2:36-44.

Jones, Ernest (1911), The Relationship between Dreams and Psychoneurotic Symptoms. *Papers on Psycho-Analysis*. London: Hogarth Press, 1948.

—— (1916), The Theory of Sublimation. *Papers on Psycho-Analysis*. London: Baillière, Tindall & Cox, 1920.

—— (1953), *The Life and Work of Sigmund Freud*, Vol. I. New York: Basic Books.

—— (1955), *The Life and Work of Sigmund Freud*, Vol. II. New York: Basic Books.

—— (1957), *The Life and Work of Sigmund Freud*, Vol. III. New York: Basic Books.

Kanzer, Mark (1957), Acting Out, Sublimation and Reality Testing. *J. Am. Psa. Assn.*, 5:404-412.

Katan, M. (1954), The Importance of the Non-Psychotic Part of the Personality in Schizophrenia. *Int. J. Psa.*, 35:119-128.

Klein, H. S. (1949), Psychogenic Factors in Dermatitis and Their Treatment by Group Therapy. *Brit. J. Med. Psychol.*, 22:32.

Kubie, Lawrence S. (1953), The Central Representation of the Symbolic Process in Psychosomatic Disorders. *Psychosom. Med.*, 15:1.

Lehn, H. K. & Menninger, Karl A.; Mayman, Martin (1950), Personality Factors in Osteoarthritis. *Assn. Res. Nerv. & Ment. Dis. Proc.*, 29:735.

Liddell, H. (1956), *Emotional Hazards in Animal and Man*. Springfield: Thomas.

Lorand, Sandor & Feldman, Sandor S. (1955), The Symbolism of Teeth in Dreams. *Int. J. Psa.*, 36:145-161.

Lowenhaupt, Elizabeth (1952), A Consideration of Psychic Mechanisms in Vasospastic Disorders of the Hand. *Psa. Rev.*, 39:329-335.

Margolin, Sydney G. (1951), The Behavior of the Stomach during Psychoanalysis. *Psa. Quart.*, 20:349-373.

———— (1953), Genetic and Dynamic Psychophysiological Determinants of Pathophysiological Processes. In: *The Psychosomatic Concept in Psychoanalysis*, ed. F. Deutsch. New York: International Universities Press.

Marmor, Judd (1949), Psychotherapy in Peptic Ulcers. *Ann. West. Med. & Surg.*, 3:166-168.

Mendelson, M. & Hirsch, S.; Webber, C. S. (1956), A Critical Examination of Some Recent Theoretical Models in Psychosomatic Medicine. *Psychosom. Med.*, 18:363-374.

Menninger, Karl A. (1938), *Man against Himself*. New York: Harcourt, Brace.

Menzer, Doris (1953), The Importance of the Psychologic Factor in Gynecology. *New Engl. J. Med.*, 249:519-522.

Menzer-Benaron, Doris & Sturgis, Somers H. (1957), Relationship between Emotional and Somatic Factors in Gynecologic Disease. *Progress in Gynecology*, 3.

Miller, Milton L. (1942), A Psychological Study of Eczema and Neurodermatitis. *Psychosom. Med.*, 4:82-93.

Mushatt, C. (1954), Psychological Aspects of Non-Specific Ulcerative Colitis. In: *Recent Developments in Psychosomatic Medicine*, ed. E. D. Wittkower & R. A. Cleghorn. New York: Lippincott.

Nacht, S. & Diatkine, R.; Favreau, J. (1956), The Ego in Perverse Relationships. *Int. J. Psa.*, 37:404-412.

Nunberg, Herman (1920), On the Catatonic Attack. In: *Practice and Theory of Psychoanalysis*. New York: International Universities Press, 1953.

———— (1949), *Problems of Bisexuality as Reflected in Circumcision*. London: Imago Publ. Co.

Penfield, W. (1958), *The Excitable Cortex in Conscious Man*. Liverpool: Liverpool University Press.

Pfister, Oskar (1912), Die Ursache der Farbenbegleitung bei akustischen Wahrnehmungen und das Wesen anderer Synästhesien. Imago, 1:265-271.

Planck, Max (1949), *Scientific Autobiography*. New York: Philosophical Library.

Richardson, Henry B. (1955), Raynaud's Phenomenon and Scleroderma. *Psa. Rev.*, 42:24-38.

Rodrigué, Emilio (1956), Notes on Symbolism. *Int. J. Psa.*, 27:147-158.

Rosen, John (1953), *Direct Analysis*. New York: Grune & Stratton.

Rosenfeld, Herbert (1952), Notes on the Psycho-Analysis of the Super-Ego Conflict in an Acute Schizophrenic Patient. *Int. J. Psa.*, 33:111-131.

Rycroft, Charles (1956), Symbolism and Its Relationship to the Primary and Secondary Processes. *Int. J. Psa.*, 37:137-146.

Sachs, G. T. L. (1912), Quoted by Hug-Hellmuth (1912).

Saul, Leon J. (1939), Hostility in Cases of Essential Hypertension. *Psychosom. Med.*, 1:153.

———— & Bernstein, C., Jr. (1941), The Emotional Settings of Some Attacks of Urticaria. *Psychosom. Med.*, 3:347.

Scarborough, L. F. (1948), Neurodermatitis from the Psychosomatic Viewpoint. *Dis. Nerv. Syst.*, 9:90-93.

Schilder, Paul (1935), *The Image and Appearance of the Human Body*. New York: International Universities Press, 1950.

Schur, Max (1955), Comments on the Metapsychology of Somatization. *The Psychoanalytic Study of the Child*, 10:119-164. New York: International Universities Press.

Schwartz, L. A. (1940), An Analyzed Case of Essential Hypertension. *Psychosom. Med.*, 2:468-486.

Segal, Hanna, (1957), Notes on Symbol Formation. *Int. J. Psa.*, 38:391-397.

Semrad, E. V. (1955), Psychopathology of Schizophrenia. *J. Clin. & Exper. Psychopathol.*, 16:10-21.

Simmel, E. (1944), Self-Preservation and the Death Instinct. *Psa. Quart.*, 13:160.

Sinnott, E. W. (1957), *Mind, Matter and Man*. New York: Harper.

Slater, E. (1953), In: *J. Ment. Sci.*, 99:44.

Sperling, Melitta (1952), A Psychoanalytic Study of Migraine and Psychogenic Headache. *Psa. Rev.*, 39:152-163.

Spitz, René A. (1946), The Smiling Response. *Genet. Psychol. Mon.*, 34:57-125.

———— (1955), The Primal Cavity: A Contribution to the Genesis of Perception and Its Role for Psychoanalytic Theory. *The Psychoanalytic Study of the Child*, 10:215-240. New York: International Universities Press.

Steinbrügge (1912), Quoted by Hug-Hellmuth (1912).

Strauss, Allan (1955), Unconscious Mental Processes and the Psycho-somatic Concept. *Int. J. Psa.*, 36:307.

Swartz, J. & Semrad, E. V. (1951), Psychosomatic Disorders in Psychoses. *Psychosom. Med.*, 13:314-321.

Thorner, H. A. (1949), Notes on a Case of Male Homosexuality. *Int. J. Psa.*, 30:31-35.

Waelder, Robert (1951), The Structure of Paranoid Ideas. *Int. J. Psa.*, 32:167.

Weisman, Avery (1956), A Study of Psychodynamics of Duodenal Ulcer Exacerbations. *Psychosom. Med.*, 18:2-41.

Weiss, E. (1923), Psychoanalysis of a Case of Nervous Asthma. *Int. J. Psa.*, 4:266.

—————— (1940), Cardiovascular Lesions of Probable Psychosomatic Origin in Arterial Hypertension. *Psychosom. Med.*, 2:249-264.

White, Benjamin V. & Cobb, Stanley; Jones, Chester M. (1939), Mucous Colitis: A Psychological Medical Study of Sixty Cases. *Psychosom. Med. Mon.* (Washington).

Wittkower, E. & Russell, B. (1953), *Emotional Factors in Skin Disease.* New York: Hoeber.

Wolf, S. (1947), Sustained Contraction of the Diaphragm: The Mechanism of a Common Type of Dyspnea and Precordial Pain. *J. Clin. Invest.*, 26:1201.

Woolhandler, H. W. (1948), Neurodermatoses. *Penna. Med. J.*, 51:1108-1113.

Zane, M. D. (1947), Psychosomatic Considerations in Peptic Ulcer. *Psychosom. Med.*, 9:372-380.

INDEX

INDEX

267